GLOBAL WARMING
THE CONTINUING DEBATE

Edited by Roger Bate

☆ ESEF ☆

The European Science
and Environment Forum

Committee:
Frits Böttcher
John Emsley
Roger Bate

Global Warming: The Continuing Debate
The European Science and Environment Forum

First published in January 1998

ISBN 0-9527734-2-2

Printed in Great Britain by Optichrome Limited, Maybury Road, Woking, Surrey, GU21 5HX

For inquiries contact ESEF, 4 Church Lane, Barton, Cambridge, England, CB3 7BE
Telephone: (+44)(0)1223 264 643 Fax: (+44)(0)1223 264 645
Web: http//:www.esef.org

Contents

II SCIENTIFIC CONTROVERSIES

Acknowledgements

I thank all the contributors to this volume. The papers make an interesting companion volume to our first, *The Global Warming Debate*. There were a number of excellent papers that we did not have room for in this edition, especially papers by Drs Dietze and Thüne. However, we hope to produce further editions on climate change and still wish potential authors to submit papers to us.

I owe special thanks to Will Sweetman and Lorraine Mooney for their work on this volume. I also thank Andrew Grice and Michael Walker for their help. Many ESEF members have commented on the papers in this volume and they have ensured the quality remains high. As if to highlight the lack of consensus over climate science, there has been much debate among the members about the scientific validity of several of the papers in this volume.

The paper by Professor Segalstad raised the most questions. Its conclusions strike at the heart of the IPCC consensus. One of the reasons for its conclusions is the response the author generated when he submitted the paper to *Nature* magazine. He was told that his paper would not be published on the following grounds: "The message of this manuscript lacks any scientific basis, and the authors ignore all the work that has been done in the past 30 years on modelling the global carbon cycle." I have shown this paper to two notable glaciologists, both of whom think the author makes an interesting contribution to knowledge. That is why we are running this paper. ESEF was established so that all well-considered views could be published and an open public debate could ensue. We, of course, welcome comments on this and other papers.

Finally, I thank the Märit and Hans Rausing Foundation for their support of this book.

As at 31st October 1997, ESEF has 110 members from 18 countries (see final pages for details of ESEF's mission).

R. N. B.
Cambridge 1997

Global Warming:
The Continuing Debate

Executive Summary

This book examines various aspects of the global warming debate. Key findings of the papers are:

The media are not fully aware of the breadth of the scientific debate on climate and hence cannot present a balanced view of it. However, they cannot be expected to shoulder all the blame for the misinformation disseminated about climate change, as pro-warming biases occur in funding, publication, presentation and policy related to the science of this issue (Bate). The media are to blame for exaggerating stories which alarm the public, and for using ad hominem attacks on sceptical scientists, rather than proper presentation of information. (Murray). Public perception is that natural disasters such as hurricanes have increased in number and intensity in recent times, and that global warming is to blame. However, the evidence for the former is mixed and for the latter is almost non-existent (Balling).

Within the scientific debate on global warming, it is often difficult to separate what the data show from what the scientists want the data to show. Pressure on scientists to provide answers has led them to underplay the remaining uncertainties, such as the role of water vapour (Spencer).

The Intergovernmental Panel on Climate Change (IPCC) uses mathematical models to produce global climate simulations, but it is here contended that these are seriously flawed, are not based on natural climate processes and hence cannot be verified using global climate data (Wiin-Christensen, Wiin-Nielsen). The Second Assessment Report (SAR), written after five years of IPCC-instigated global climate policy, devotes its third chapter to measurement of climatic data. However, it does not pay enough attention to random variations in natural climatic processes, hence changes are tacitly assumed to be caused by human activity (Gordon).

Chapter 8 of SAR, which deals with attribution and causes of climate change, concludes that "the balance of the evidence suggests a discernible human influence on global climate". This conclusion is shown to be flawed, as the underlying natural variation has not been estimated. Perhaps ozone loss-induced stratospheric cooling and some sulphate-induced cooling in the

Northern hemisphere can be attributed to human activity, but the so-called fingerprint of human impact from greenhouse gas-induced warming is "smudged". It is not the clear signal that Chapter 8 or the policymakers' summary would lead us to believe. The authors of Chapter 8 were drawing on their own research and reviewing it, a non-standard scientific procedure. (Weber, Bate).

Voluminous climate data provided from satellite remote sensing is stretching even the vast increases in computing power in the past decade, and it is far outstripping the ability of analysts to usefully process that information. Yet projections of climate change are fraught with difficulties because of the dearth of quality historic data (Vaughan).

Solar-terrestrial cycles can explain variations in the earth's climate (Landscheidt). A coupled solar-greenhouse model explains variations in temperature far better than greenhouse gas on its own, and solar models are individually better at explaining variations than are greenhouse gas models (Posmentier et al). Development of sophisticated models linking solar changes to climatic changes on earth, show that long run predictions of major changes are possible, where analysis of meteorological data fail. Landcheidt's solar model far outperforms the models promoted by the IPCC.

If climate change does turn out to be a problem, ocean fertilisation with iron is a cheaper and politically less intrusive method of removing emissions than control by taxation. It also exploits excess CO_2 as a resource for enhancing ocean fisheries (Singer).

Finally, the contemporary hypothesis that CO_2 atmospheric concentration has increased due to human fossil fuel emissions by about 25% in the last century is incorrect: 4% would be a more accurate estimate (Segalstad).The hypothesis is flawed because carbon dioxide remains in the atmosphere for only about 5 years, not 50 years or more, as claimed by the IPCC. This is supported by evidence from both radioactive and stable carbon isotopes. Natural causes are far more likely to have caused the recent increase in measurable CO_2.

The Politicisation of Climate Science

Roger Bate
Director
European Science and Environment Forum

Summary

The general public seems to believe that the climate is changing due to human activities. They hear from their politicians, environmental groups and the media that those changes will be harmful and that we should be doing something about it. However, within the scientific community things are not so clear cut. This volume of papers suggests that the existing scientific evidence does not support the call for urgent action, and that the conventional picture of climate science is a false one. While the media deserves its fair share of the blame for common misconceptions, it is only partially to blame. David Murray's paper explains their culpability particularly well. The scientists, or more accurately the science bureaucracy, are in large part to blame for public misunderstanding. In the area of climate, political and economic pressures have corrupted the science. The main concern of my preface is to explain why this has occurred in the climate debate (see Bate, 1996 for more details).

Corrupted science

Science is a discovery process in which hypotheses are put forward, tested through empirical research and then revised to reflect the findings. Corrupted science, however, is science that does not move from hypothesis to data to conclusion, but from mandated or politically acceptable conclusion back to selected data in order to reach the mandated or acceptable conclusion. It is a backwards method in which the 'right' answers are known before the right questions are asked. Corrupted science not only misrepresents the true state of knowledge, but also the scientific process itself. The selectivity of its process is denied and dissenting perspectives are excluded due to the need for 'approved' conclusions.

There is little doubt that this tendency is extremely dangerous, for it undermines the scientific process and threatens the ability of science to provide insights and answers about the world around us. Insofar as science becomes a tool for political agendas of any stripe, its value as a social institution is diminished.

The Model of the Future

Climate science is about the future and what will happen there, so that is where my discussion begins.

Any successful strategist, from a chess player to a world leader, will think ahead, use 'what if' scenarios, and second guess others' reactions or feedbacks. In short, we seek to plan for the events that lie ahead. Thus scientists and other academics seek to develop models of the future in order to know what to expect.

Economics, for example, has great analytical value where inputs are known, or can be reasonably estimated. But to try to produce a definitive socio-economic forecast is tricky. Making bold predictions about future trends when even the direction of change is unknown can only damage the credibility of the discipline in the long run. Thus, economists give best and worse case scenarios, and lay out their premises – some of which they know may be wrong – and acknowledge their uncertainties. Were they to do otherwise, uncertainties would become assumptions, which would be used as a basis for economic computer models, which produce concise answers that appear to be authoritative. The basic assumptions would be inevitably forgotten and the answers swallowed whole without the required amount of salt.

Most climate modellers have followed a similar course, making predictions with the appropriate caveats and underlining the uncertainties. Others have not been so circumspect, which is exactly how the global warming scare started. The level of uncertainty in climate science is such that it is unable to predict even the direction, let alone the magnitude, of a physical change. Scientists still do not know much about natural feedback mechanisms within the climate, and the myriad variables that these can affect. See Wiin-Christensen and Wiin-Nielsen's chapter for an excellent discussion of the limits of our current knowledge.

Take the example of regional rainfall. Primitive computer models of the mid-80s predicted metres of inundation coinciding with whole degrees of temperature rise. The picture was of a climate catastrophe. Yet with every improvement in modelling technique, these predictions have become more modest: metres have become centimetres; degrees, tenths of degrees; and so on. The models are still not up to the job of 'predicting' past weather, but the genie is out of the bottle. Global warming is a political issue and thus has a life of its own outside and beyond science. Climate change, as we must call it, has become a juggernaut, not only in the policy process, but also in the scientific community.

Who gains?

Despite the shortcomings of economic forecasting – economic trends are no less uncertain than climatic trends – there is a branch of economics that offers insight into the climate change debate. Public choice theory explains why an understanding of the incentive structures facing scientists, politicians, pressure groups and businessmen is important to understanding the political dynamic on a given issue. Although public choice is often ignored by policy makers and economists alike it has a rigorous basis; one of its originators, James Buchanan, won the Nobel Prize in 1986 for his work in this area. Public choice theory can provide important insights about the actions of all the players in the climate debate, and I have documented this analysis elsewhere (Bate, 1996).

Public choice theory recognises that individuals act in their own interest. It is conventional wisdom (at least in Europe) that public servants apply their professional training and expertise in the public interest and not in their own, that government works on behalf of the people for the people.

Public choice theorists argue that this view is naïve. They examine the individuals involved in the making and executing of public policies and the incentives they face. Public choice finds that most people, most of the time, find it impossible to argue against their own perceived interests for any sustained period. Although one's self interest may include family interests and even community interest, it also includes economic interest. The bottom line of public choice is that bureaucrats are just like everyone else: they respond to incentives and pursue their perceived self-interest.

The public choice model of political decision-making divides society into four groups – voters, politicians, bureaucrats and interest groups. All these actors are assumed to want something from the system: voters want better government, politicians want votes, bureaucrats want job security and enlarged budgets, interest groups want income. Politicians, bureaucrats and interest groups have distinct advantages over the voters. All of them are professionals who will know more about their specialist subject than the average voter who remains rationally ignorant on most policy issues. The global warming issue involves all these actors, vying in a game of competing interests.

Climate Interest Groups

Because of the numerous groups acting in the climate change debate, the result is a political process driven by perverse incentives. Climate change could affect everyone. However, most individuals are not, nor can they be, directly involved in the policy debate, which is why they remain uninformed. Those with a direct interest include energy suppliers, other affected sectors (insurance, banking, transport etc.), those whose business is the protection of the natural environment, and those with more subtle incentives. The latter include the scientists, the science-led bureaucracies and political entrepreneurs. They are treated less critically by the media, and as a result their credibility is enhanced, even though their motives are not necessarily any purer, than the motives of those with an obvious financial gain.

Businessmen face clear incentives on climate change. Solar, hydro, and nuclear power executives want it to be real, so that their businesses can thrive, while oil and coal executives hope that talk of climate change is nothing but hot air. Other businesses have mixed positions but most back the coal and oil position, even if not strongly. Evidence for this is the strong public stance taken by the CEOs of the American Business Roundtable against a climate treaty.

Similarly, green pressure groups can gain kudos and budgets for promoting climate change. Fund-raising is easier in a crisis, and where debate attracts publicity. As U.S. Interior Secretary Bruce Babbitt, himself the former head of the League of Conservation Voters, remarked, "The bottom line for environmentalists is how do you induce people to send money to sustain the movement." (Adler, 1995. See also the discussion therein on the falling fortunes of environmental organisations.) Thus, environmental groups issue direct mail appeals and take out advertisements hyping fears of a greenhouse catastrophe, demonstrating the need for their continued vigilance. After all, if there is no crisis, what need have we for Greenpeace?

Politicians also have much to gain. Any facing credibility problems at home may seek to become statesmen in the international arena – an arena in which they are less accountable for their actions. They can sign treaties that their citizens have heard little about, and which will not take affect for years to come, after the political leaders are safely out of office. Those politicians fortunate enough to be representing countries that will meet their emissions targets can score additional green points from acting in their national interest anyway. Many mistakenly believe global trade to be a zero sum game, and that by demanding urgent action on global warming from other countries they will benefit at home, especially where CO_2 reduction measures are not yet in place. Thus, at the July 1997 United Nations 'Rio plus 5' summit in New York, British Prime Minister Tony Blair admonished the US for its energy profligacy, as did German Chancellor Helmut Kohl. Left unsaid was that the UK and Germany will meet their emission reduction targets because of non-environmental factors. The demise of the coal industry in the UK due to Margaret Thatcher's market liberalisation, and the failure of East German industry have more to do with declining emissions than any environmental leadership in Europe.

The above incentives are rather clear. Yet academics have remained above suspicion, especially in Europe. Objectivity in science comes from open debate; credibility comes from peer review. Scientists' integrity rests on this debate and peer-review process. Anything which compromises these precious, if not unique, qualities, surely threatens the public's trust in science's pronouncements. One would therefore assume that scientists would be relatively immune to public choice pressures, but while they may be less subject to such incentives than other groups, they are nonetheless human.

Climate change involves a myriad of scientific disciplines, but is dominated by just a few, the most important being dynamic mathematical modelling, not because it is more important to knowledge than other sciences, but because it is the one discipline that purports to provide the vision of the future wanted by the media, and by the political system.

Unlike international trade, short-run government science funding is often a zero-sum game. Determining who gets what slice of the pie is a decision based upon many criteria, including the political relevance of the science. There is no doubt that dynamic modelling can be more relevant to policy than, say, paleobotany, and it has received the lion's share of climate funding in recent years – at the expense of other disciplines, increased overall funding notwithstanding. There is only so much research money to go around.

Scientists cannot but be aware of this fact. If there is less need for their discipline or their research, there will be less money to fund their endeavours. For instance, the Hadley Centre at the UK Meteorological Office exists largely because of climate change and the money it brings in. If climate change were suddenly to disappear as an issue, Hadley might even close, with its multi-million pound annual budget allocated to other research. The Max Planck Institute in Germany and the University of East Anglia in the UK are two other major European research centres that have benefited from climate change.

Scientists lucky enough to be in disciplines related to global warming, and there are lots of them, have prospered in the last ten years, much to the chagrin of scientists in less fashionable fields whose work may well be of more immediate and likely importance. More is spent on climate research in the UK, for example, than is spent on cancer research. So, those at the mercy of the fickle funder are wise to keep doubts to themselves. All these incentives and reactions to them are predictable by public choice theory

In short, big science, such as big computer models, requires big money. Competition for funding is intense. In this situation, publicity and 'policy relevance' help in the scramble for funds - climate change has both. Due to their success in capturing funding, many climate scientists' careers now depend on global warming. So scientists, along with business and political players (and the media, another interest group that merits a discussion all its own) have an interest in how information about climate change is presented. In such an environment, formal scientific procedures and peer review become that much more important, and deviations from accepted procedural norms become inherently suspect.

Peer Review Problems

The issue of peer review itself is an important one, and shows the biases inherent in modern science. Scientists often blame the media for exaggerating stories of alarm, but of course it is not just the media that like exciting 'positive' results. Editors of scientific journals enjoy the attention that publication of exciting or groundbreaking research can bring.

A recent paper in the science journal *Oikos* explained how research which is important, but not exciting or innovative, seldom makes it into the more prestigious scientific journals. Those journals rarely carry papers where the findings are largely 'negative.' For example, a researcher might analyse the data relating to the link between pesticide residues in apples and bladder cancer, and conclude that his results indicated no correlation. One would think that the information discovered by the researcher would be useful for those working in the relevant fields. But the results are just not exciting, and the chance of the paper being published in a top journal like *Nature* is remote. To come to this conclusion, the study's authors analysed 1,812 scientific papers published between 1989 and 1995 picked at random from 40 biology journals. Only 9% of the papers contained 'non-significant' results; the figure was even lower for the most prestigious journals (Csada et. al., 1996).

Given the pressure on university researchers to publish – and in good journals – the bias against publishing 'negative' results has some worrying implications. First, it is likely that the hypotheses to be tested will be conservative, because 'positive' results will seem more likely in such cases. More outlandish hypotheses – ones that, if proven, might broaden the scientific picture – will not be entertained. Second, researchers are likely to select the data carefully in search of a 'significant' correlation. If the chance of being published is increased by showing a 'positive' result, researchers will be tempted to trawl through the data until they find one – ignoring all the negative correlation they encounter on the way. Careers may depend on such things.

So while the media want alarming or positive result stories, so do the best journals. Saying that an ice-shelf has become larger, tree lines and temperatures were higher in the past, or that uncertainties remain, is simply not good enough to attract attention to one's research. Is it any wonder that academic refutations of the climate thesis are comparatively rare? A fair representation of the peer-reviewed literature would in any case be biased in favour of global warming, so there would be even less need to fiddle with reports.

Climate Consensus?

Prompted by funding applications from US climate modellers in the late 1970s, two United Nations bodies – the World Meteorological Organisation (WMO) and the UN Environment Programme (UNEP) – embraced climate research. In 1988, as global warming was fast becoming a prominent issue, these two bodies set up the Intergovernmental Panel on Climate Change (IPCC) as a 'mechanism aimed at providing the basis for the development of a realistic and effective internationally accepted strategy for addressing climate change.' Note that even then there was an underlying assumption that 'climate change' was a given fact that needed to be 'addressed' by international action.

With its assumptions in hand, the machine trundled on, commissioning research, holding international meetings in exotic locations and producing a series of reports on the state of climate science and various policy options. The hallmark of these reports, according to Massachusetts Institute of Technology meteorology professor Richard Lindzen, were 'waffle statements which don't say anything, which nobody can disagree with' (Wilkie, 1995).

Things changed with the IPCC's Second Assessment Report in 1995. It stated that '[t]he balance of the evidence suggests that there is a discernible human influence on global climate.' This statement was seized upon by environmental interest groups and the press as final evidence of a scientific consensus on climate change. This statement, environmental leaders announced, was definitive proof that urgent action was warranted. However, was the 'scientific consensus' supporting this view politically engineered? The contributing scientists themselves were expressing quiet but firm uncertainty.

The credibility of any source of scientific information is important. Most commentators assume that scientific documents are based on science, not politics, and, hence are objective. The IPCC is seen as providing a politically relevant consensus view, in part because it relies upon the scientific peer-review process. Everything is read, discussed, modified and approved by a panel of experts. Its reputation hangs on this critical approach and its adherence to strict governmental review procedures. But as one IPCC lead author, Dr. Keith Shine of Reading University, described the process of producing the IPCC Policymakers' summary: 'We produce a draft, and then the policymakers go through it line by line and change the way it is presented . . . They don't change the data, but the way it's represented. It is peculiar that they have the final say in what goes into a scientists' report' (Winton, 1995). The science is scientific, but the spin placed upon it is political (Grubb, 1996).

The main report approved by the world's governments at the IPCC plenary meeting in Madrid 1995, published in July 1996, included alarmist post-plenary changes that did not allow wide scrutiny. Gone from the final report is any meaningful emphasis of the uncertainties about man-made climate change and gone are concerns about unwarranted conclusions being drawn from the studies. In November 1995, the underlying report did not state that human-induced climate change had occurred; since July 1996, with no new data to consider, it does. (Singer, 1996; Financial Times, 1996).

Certain sentences, such as the following, were deleted from the report: 'None of the studies has shown clear evidence that we can attribute the observed changes to the specific cause of increases in greenhouse gases.' This statement was replaced with:

'If the observed global mean changes over the last 20 to 50 years cannot be fully explained by natural climate variability, some (unknown) fraction of the changes must be due to human influences.' (IPCC 1995, 8.4.2.1). The draft conclusion to the report was completely deleted as well. (See Weber's paper for more details).

It is worth noting that the 1995 IPCC report also allowed unpublished papers to form the basis of its conclusions. For example, Chapter 6 of the Second Assessment Report contains 22 references to papers which had not passed peer-review at the time of publication. I asked the head of the scientific working group of the IPCC about peer-review and post-plenary changes when I debated him in December 1996. His answer reveals a lot. He acknowledged that they were not peer-reviewed but were readily available to all IPCC reviewers. But IPCC reviewers would have had to know of the existence of these papers – which most probably did not – and then request them. Any wider comment on the papers was impossible.

The timing of the deletions and alterations suggests that liberties were taken with procedure, perhaps in order to achieve the required consensus. Policymakers, and the plethora of applied scientists and socio-economic specialist advisors, welcomed the IPCC conclusions and glossed over the irregularities. Instead they concentrated on attacking the industry lobbyists who pointed the changes out, invoking what is known in the UK as the Keeler principle – "well they would say that wouldn't they" – or dismissing critics as practitioners of 'tobacco science.'

The IPCC's indiscretions seem to be rubbing off on its founder organisation, the UNEP. In September 1997, scientists working for UNEP's report on the ozone depleter, methyl bromide, were concerned about the way the document had been altered, much like the IPCC document. Consultants to UNEP say that the rewritten documents dishonestly overstate the potential for the introduction of substitutes for methyl bromide, which may cause up to a tenth of all ozone depletion.

An angry letter was sent to UNEP in late August 1997 by 22 member scientists of its methyl bromide technical options committee. They expressed 'deep and serious concerns' that their report, drafted in February, had been 'unilaterally rewritten' without their consent. The scientists further claimed that because of the new version of the report, UNEP would advise ministers that the world could achieve a 75% reduction in the use of methyl bromide by 2001. At the tenth meeting of the Montreal Protocol on substances hazardous to the ozone layer which began in mid-September 1997, ministers voted to eliminate the chemical, which is used to fumigate soil and processed foods, by 2005.

Writing in *New Scientist*, Fred Pearce (1997) interviewed one of the committee's scientists, Colin Smith of the British pest control company, Rentokil. Smith was quoted as saying, 'this is totally contrary to everything that has been agreed by the experts in the options committee'. Smith resigned in August 1997 from the committee in protest. He alleges that pressure from US officials led UNEP to subvert the report in order to promote the notion that an early ban on methyl bromide was possible. The US had already agreed to ban methyl bromide use from 2001. Under pressure from its powerful agricultural lobby and the Environmental Protection Agency, the US wanted its farmers to be protected by forcing the rest of the world to follow suit. Smith explained that a significant sentence warning of a 'lack of practical alternatives [to methyl bromide] for [fumigating] dried fruits and nuts as well as spices and processed foods' was deleted. Without the report alterations it is doubtful that methyl bromide would have been phased out as quickly.

Climate change document alterations will have a far greater impact than over one chemical, albeit an important one. As national officials rely on the exact wording of the report they sign their names to, the reports should be finished when they are approved drafts. It should be clear that post-plenary alterations actually undermine the entire IPCC negotiating process. Government officials will be less likely to approve documents in the future if they are under the impression that it will be tampered with after signature.

It is interesting to note that the breaches of climate treaty protocol were noticed first in the US, not in Europe. Is there a greater trust in Europe of professional hierarchies? Trust of officialdom and the United Nations may not be high in Europe, but it is far lower in the USA. Perhaps this has led to the science debate being much less open in Europe than in the US.

Conclusion

For the past decade, the climate debate has centred on modelled forecasts and some climate science. Obfuscation and myth-making have flourished. Consensus is now equated with truth. The source of the science has become more important than the content, and peer review has been used as a political weapon. Those from business have been decried as special pleaders unless they back green claims, and have even spawned their own fifth columnists (environmental managers) whose own jobs depend on the climate business. But, nevertheless the debate continues. The European Science and Environment Forum (ESEF) seeks to keep the scientific debate alive in Europe, so that there is not a premature rush to implement costly policies. Given that pro-warming biases appear in funding, publication, presentation and in policy, we think this a vitally important action to be undertaken.

Roger Bate

Roger Bate is Director of the Environment Unit at the Institute of Economic Affairs and a Director of ESEF. He is the author of several academic papers on science policy and economic issues, and has published numerous articles in papers such as the *Wall Street Journal* and the *Sunday Times*. He appears frequently on television and radio, and is a fellow of the Royal Society of Arts.

References

Adler, J. (1995) 'Environmentalism at the Crossroads' (Washington DC, CEI).

Bate, R, (1996) 'Science Under Siege', *Energy and Environment*, 7 (4)

Boehmer-Christiansen, Sonja, (1996) 'Political Pressure in the Formation of Scientific Consensus,' *The Global Warming Debate: The Report of the European Science and Environment Forum*, John Emsley, ed., (London: ESEF).

Csada, R. D., P.C. Jams and R.H.M. Espie, (1997) 'The 'file drawer problem' of non-significant results: does it apply to biological research,' *Oikos*, vol. 76, no. 3.

Financial Times, *Climate Change 1995*, Energy Economist Briefings, (London: FT Energy Publishing, 1996).

Grubb, Michael, (1996) 'Purpose and function of IPCC,' *Nature*, vol. 379, 108,.

IPCC, Summary for Policymakers of the Contribution of Working Group 1 to the Second Assessment Report to the Intergovernmental Panel on Climate Change, 1996, United Nations.

IPCC Second Assessment Report, 1995. Approved at the fifth session of IPCC WGI Madrid, 27-29 November 1995, United Nations.

Pearce, Fred, *New Scientist*, 30th August 1997, page 18.

Singer, S. Fred, (1996) 'A Preliminary Critique of IPCC's Second Assessment of Climate Change,' *The Global Warming Debate: The Report of the European Science and Environment Forum*, John Emsley, ed. (London: ESEF,).

Wilkie, Tom, 'Science 'using language of the adman',' *The Independent* (London), December 1, 1995.

Winton, Neil, 'Global warming theory just hot air, some experts say,' *Reuters World Service*, December 20, 1995.

Warm Front: Print Media and Climate Change Coverage

David Murray
Director of Research
Statistical Assessment Service
Washington DC
USA

Is there a problem with the reporting of global warming? Is a fair and accurate portrait of the scientific issues, and the dominant opinion of the scientific community, being conveyed to the consuming public? Throughout the last two years we have been asking these questions, and have investigated the possibilities by an examination of newspapers, news magazines, and science journals.

There appear to be two evaluations of the media process, and while both agree that there is a problem, they arrive at different conclusions as to just what has gone wrong. According to journalist Ross Gelbspan, there is a problem with the media and climate change – the problem is that the handful of minor sceptics backed by industry are getting altogether too much coverage and credibility. Gelbspan himself, meanwhile, actually makes news with the claim that sceptics are dominating the media debate. The sceptics are successful, Gelbspan argues, because they pitch their campaign to "older, less educated males, and younger females." (In fact, studies of climate sceptics among readers show them to be more educated than the general population).

Interestingly, Gelbspan's argument that the problem with media coverage is simply that sceptics are allowed to suggest an absence of consensus and conclusiveness on the part of climate scientists is shared by Colin Macilwain of the journal *Nature*. In a personal communication Macilwain complained that too many journalists had succumbed to the notion that there was even a dispute any longer about anthropogenic warming, and he echoed Gelbspan's charge that the cause was bad-faith lobbying by industry.

Also agreeing is Bud Ward, editor of the *Environment Writer*. Ward explains what it is about journalists that creates this unbalanced coverage accorded the climate minority: "sceptics have an impact disproportionate to their numbers," he says, because of American journalists' "tendency to accentuate extremes so as to get both sides of the story. In this area of journalism, balance is the enemy of accuracy."

Yet others argue that the problem of media coverage lies elsewhere; in fact, they see a pattern opposite to the one described by Gelbspan, whereby the dominant media have not only been neglectful of the full story, but have actively muzzled contrary information at the same time that they have credulously swallowed and amplified tenuous positive evidence. These critics perceive a one-way ratchet that shows the media more in the role of an advocate in a courtroom, than as a balanced referee. Indeed, many journalists are accused of serving as a prosecuting attorney, seeking always for confirmatory evidence, always parrying doubt, uncertainty or evidence that fails to convict.

In our experience of journalists, many seem to be practising a version of what is termed 'rational ignorance': the use of stereotype and prejudice as a rational response to a world overwhelming in detail or too challenging in scientific appraisal. In order to make sense of a landscape changing too rapidly and too technically challenging, many journalists have adopted the expedient of awarding black hats and white hats, of choosing villains and heroes, so as to save themselves the trouble and the confusion of the independent evaluation on its merits which each new scientific report would otherwise command. The news media, it seems, could not operate without such a filtering system that screens stories, in a largely unconscious manner.

In this respect, reporters are like trout in a media stream, watching upriver for whatever tasty morsel the current will bring to them, occasionally actively foraging under a root or lily pad. Fishermen are numerous, though the sight of a hat rim over the bank's edge will likely spook the fish. The skill in acquiring media coverage lies, as any good public relations officer knows, in how you tie your flies.

In the global warming debate, some bait has been taken, some rejected. Most intriguing, however, is that the bait presented to reporters is not perceived by them to be bait at all, but rather just a sample of their natural food.

Let us examine a particular piece of reportage to see what can go wrong. The story is by John Fialka of the *Wall Street Journal* and it appeared August 26, 1997. The focus was on the difficulty that Vice President Al Gore was having convincing the public about the dangers of global warming. Perversely, however,

Fialka provides in a single sentence a sample of just why the public might well be confused: "While the majority of climate scientists now predict the economic damage from the man-made output of this pollutant (carbon dioxide) – largely from burning fossil fuels – will be severe, it is expected to come on gradually as the sea level inches upward, as storms become more violent, and as agricultural land begins to dry out."

Observers close to the issue should realise that several dimensions of the global warming story have here been collapsed into a single indictment. First, there is the question as to whether warming has occurred and over which time scale – the last 100 years (most probably) or over the last 50 years (not at all clear). Though we have a sense of what the IPCC participants believe, no one has established what the "majority of climate scientists" actually think on this score. Mr. Fialka, in a personal interview, states that he meant to refer to the "2,700 climate scientists who recently signed a letter to the President on the economic impact of climate change." Unfortunately, the document in question, a project of Ozone Action, involves nowhere near that number of actual climate scientists.

Second, if there has been warming, there is the question of anthropogenicity – are man-made greenhouse gases implicated in a causal role, or is that 'signal' against the background of natural variation still ambiguous? Again, there is no firm consensus, though Fialka confidently asserts that "damage ... largely from burning fossil fuels," must therefore be anthropogenic.

Third (and I will bypass the accuracy of referring to carbon dioxide as an environmental 'pollutant'), there is the question that specific weather effects of presumed warming – more violent storms, rising sea levels, and drying agricultural land – are not uniformly predicted by all models (for instance, many models show, rather than drying, an increase in vegetative density in key agricultural areas).

Fourth, and finally, establishing the economic consequence of these changes, itself an ambiguous exercise, is the province not of the IPCC climate scientists' panel, but of a separate working group. Again, we simply have no idea what the majority of climate scientists predict about "economic damage."

But Mr. Fialka, a most able environmental journalist, has had lots of 'official' help in arriving at his condensed and misleading version of where things stand in climate change. Not only are journalists vulnerable to the editorial choices of science journals and the spin offered by pressure groups and their public relations allies, they also find themselves at the mercy of information provided by government agencies.

Surely most environmental journalists have at this point heard and accepted the 1995 IPCC declaration that "the balance of evidence suggests a discernible human influence" on climate change. But few indeed are likely to have read the sentences from the notorious 'amended' chapter 8 of the IPCC report that were deleted. For instance, following the statement that, "To date, pattern-based studies have not been able to quantify the magnitude of a greenhouse gas or aerosol effect on climate," the IPCC report had contained the following lines; "No study to date has positively attributed all or part [of the climate changes observed to date] to anthropogenic causes. None of the studies cited above has shown clear evidence that we can attribute the observed (climate) changes to the specific cause of increases of greenhouse gases." If the IPCC report was in fact expurgated with an eye to media sound bites, it certainly has worked.

An additional example of how misleading information can be fed to journalists from a seemingly reputable government source is found in the U.S. Global Change Research Program document 'Our Changing Planet,' a report by the subcommittee on global change research, the Committee on Environment and Natural Resources of the National Science and Technology Council. The document touts on its back cover two maps of the U.S. showing increases in vegetation density under two separate global warming scenarios – the NOAA Geophysical Fluid Dynamics Laboratory (GFDL) and the United Kingdom Meteorological Office (UKMO).

The projections are devastating, suggesting that, for instance, large portions of Texas and California would experience a warming-induced vegetation increase of greater than 200%, while Minnesota and Michigan would experience a 75% decrease. The reason these projected changes are so dramatic, however, is revealed by the model assumptions underlying the two scenarios. Based upon an assumed doubling of CO_2, the GFDL model produces an average increase in temperature of 4.3°C (7.7°F); the UKMO model predicts an even higher effect of 6.7°C (12°F).

Both these models are well known to make predictions much higher than current generation models, and are widely considered by climate scientists to be not only out-of-date but misleadingly high in their temperature projections. When asked about the choice of such model projections, project co-ordinator Rick Piltz of the White House Office of Science and Technology

Policy answered that there was "a time-lag between the climate science and the ecological and economic analyses."

Not only are journalists provided with misleading information from official political sources, they may also find that the scientific journals themselves provide a selective view of research. A good example of the way in which tenuous science has become irrefutable wisdom can be found in a *Nature* correspondence by researcher Camille Parmesan (August 1996), arguing that butterfly extinction within its west coast range was plausibly a function of global warming.

Demurrals, contrary information, and challenges by many researchers were ignored by *Nature*, and never received media coverage. In fact, I received a letter in response to my statistical re-analysis of the Parmesan data from a *Nature* reviewer asserting that while I was right, the issue was moot, since "no one now thinks that her argument is sustainable." Yet the butterfly claims are now, nearly a year after the fact, surely embedded in conventional journalistic wisdom. They were most recently asserted without qualification by Bill McKibben in the *New York Times*, and reiterated by Associated Press science writer Matt Crenson in a special article of July 13, 1997 on the effects of warming. Crenson argues that the signs of climate change are everywhere more visible: "From Alaska to Mexico, ecologists are finding provocative signs that global warming may be altering North America's flora and fauna. Seabirds in California and Oregon have been devastated by a slight warming of the water off the Pacific coast...vigorous tree growth threatens alpine meadows; in Montana, glaciers are melting at an alarming rate.. And they worry.... that plants and animals will be pushed to the limit. On the West Coast, the range of Edith's checkerspot butterfly seems to be gradually moving northward..."

It is worth examining this particular story in detail, for rarely has a piece of research received the immediate and widespread publicity that this modest study did. In August 1996 Parmesan, a biologist at the University of California at Santa Barbara, published, in a brief discussion in the famous British science journal, her observations of the movements of a butterfly - the Edith's checkerspot - found in the American west. She observed that overall the butterfly had moved north by about one hundred miles; she suggested that this northward movement resulted from climatic warming. She also found that the butterfly was now extinct in a number of more southerly locations in which it had previously been found: "Sites where previously recorded populations still existed were on average 2 [degrees Celsius] further north than sites where populations were extinct. Populations in Mexico were four times more likely to be extinct than those in Canada."

Parmesan did not make outlandish claims for the significance of her finding about one sort of butterfly. Instead, she declared that "conclusive evidence for or against the existence of the predicted biological effects of climate change will come...from replication of this type of study with additional taxa [that is, varieties of animals] in other regions." On the other hand, she did argue that the evidence to which she pointed "suggests climate change as the cause of the observed range shift [of the checkerspot]." And she concluded by declaring that "the evidence presented here provides the clearest indication to date that global climate warming is already influencing species' distributions."

In short, Parmesan made an interesting and provocative claim about the possible implications of the movement of a single species of butterfly. Still, the attention that her study received is surprising. *Nature* is a weekly journal offering an excellent overview of developments throughout the scientific world. Every issue contains many interesting and provocative claims, few of which are ever reported on by major news outlets. Parmesan's communication, however, was covered in a lengthy story (lengthier, in fact, than the communication itself) in the *New York Times'* weekly Tuesday science section. Her finding was also reported in newspapers like the *Atlanta Constitution* (in a front-page article), *Baltimore Sun, Los Angeles Times,* and *Washington Post.*

In other words, major news outlets heavily publicised a suggestive finding that by the researcher's own admission needed to be replicated to be at all conclusive. If one swallow does not a summer make, it is at least as true that one butterfly does not a global warming prove. Nevertheless, Parmesan's preliminary finding became an important news story.

Furthermore, Parmesan's finding was not only preliminary, but also questionable. Most notably, she took it for granted that the climate had warmed in the locales in which the checkerspot was now extinct. In fact, however, West Coast temperatures do not appear to have warmed at all between 1909 and 1994, once one adjusts for growing urbanisation: a temperature increase resulting from the construction of pavement, heated buildings, and night lights is not attributable to greenhouse gases. A recent communication in the Bulletin of the American

Meteorological Society concluded that "the apparent global warming" is in reality "urban waste heat affecting only urban areas" in California, Oregon, Washington and British Columbia.

It should be clear that these temperature records squarely contradict Parmesan's interpretation of the evidence. For regardless of whether Edith's checkerspot thinks globally, it must act locally. So even if warming is occurring on a global basis, it cannot explain the butterfly's range shift unless it has also taken place locally: a warming that has not affected rural southern California cannot explain the butterfly's departure from sites there. It cannot, that is, unless we assume that the Edith's checkerspot is an avid newspaper reader: in that case, media reports of the reality of warming perhaps convinced it to ignore the evidence of its own senses.

Furthermore, it is not clear that warming - assuming for the moment that it occurred - would be the factor responsible for the butterfly's range shift. In Parmesan's understanding, warming is the proximate cause of the butterfly's range shift; but the direct cause is the alteration of suitable plant - caused by warming - that had formerly hosted it. Thus Parmesan took pains to exclude from consideration sites from which the butterfly had departed, when the host plant had disappeared as a result of "human activities such as land-clearing construction, overgrazing and introduction of exotic plants."

But human activities - rather than warming - could arguably still be responsible for much of the range shift in the sites that Parmesan did consider. Even if development did not harm the host plants, changes in air quality or the impact of agricultural chemicals might still account for the butterfly's extinction in sites that were being developed. It is at least suggestive that many of the southern sites from which the checkerspot has departed are adjacent to San Diego and Los Angeles.

Finally, it is hard to know what to make of Parmesan's finding, because her communication did not include anything like a baseline for the number of extinctions that would be expected in the absence of any warming - assuming once again that warming actually took place. Was warming responsible for many of the local extinctions? It's hard to be certain, unless we have a sense of how many extinctions would have occurred normally, even in the absence of warming.

For all of these reasons, Parmesan's conclusion about the impact of warming, while interesting, is eminently debatable. Yet preliminary research subjected to a debatable interpretation was unquestioningly reported in major newspapers. Although a few of the stories explained that some scientists were unsure of the impact of the climate on the checkerspot, for the most part the media raised no doubts while publicising Parmesan's findings widely.

The interesting question, of course, is what would have happened had Parmesan's finding called into question - rather than seeming to confirm - the impact of global warming. Suppose that Parmesan had found that the checkerspot was shifting southward rather than northward. That would have been an equally important observation. Would it have been covered in the *New York Times*? For that matter, would her research have appeared in *Nature* in the first place?

We obviously cannot answer that question conclusively, but it is still worth raising. Certainly one can suspect that research conforming to the global-warming scenario is greeted more favourably in many newsrooms than research contradicting it. Be that as it may, disproportionate coverage of a preliminary research finding is always unwelcome - no matter what belief the finding may seem to bolster.

So is there a selective filter in operation with regard to global warming research? Those unhappy with media coverage of warming issues have several theories of how journalists operate. A perceived imbalance could result from a variety of problems, ranging from laziness to outright ideological bias on the part of reporters. Many critics think of journalists as contrarians by nature, inclined to run stories that challenge conventional wisdom. If this were true, however, greenhouse sceptics should have little trouble getting their point of view in print, since the majority view seems to be that warming is a settled issue.

But an examination of which scientific facts get selected and which are ignored in press coverage shows that the supposition of a contrarian approach explains little. Journalists seem to operate in many instances with selective filters whose exact nature is difficult to determine, but which serve to screen some stories from view while accelerating others into prominence. Some lessons about journalistic practice can be learned from comparing in juxtaposition stories that 'made the cut' or did not.

The first example is a press release (June 24, 1997) from the Science and Environmental Policy Project (SEPP) announcing that "Global Warming, If It Occurs, Could Lower Sea Levels," The news could very well have attracted attention, since it is clearly 'contrarian' and journalists are supposed to appreciate challenges to conventional wisdom. But in fact there was virtual silence on the part of the media.

A journalist who declined to report the press release could plausibly argue that the analysis was only 'in submission' to a journal, and hence had not achieved standing in the scientific community. Yet other pieces of contrarian evidence that were published in reputable journals were similarly ignored if they failed to sustain the dominant interpretation of climate change. A recent example would be an article that appeared in *Geophysical Research Letters* (vol.23, no. 10, May 15, 1996) by Yale University researchers Michael E. Mann and Jeffrey Park entitled "Greenhouse Warming and Changes in the Seasonal Cycle of Temperature: Model Versus Observation." Mann and Park examine the claim that the greenhouse effect may be altering the seasonal cycle, and note that, contrary to expectations, "Significant phase delays (i.e., later seasonal transitions) are found in the simulations, opposite to the phase advances isolated in the observations.... Much of the variability in the observational data is not predicted in the models."

The burden of the piece is to note the incompatibility of model outcomes with observational data, suggesting the inadequacy of modellers' assumptions. So here is published science appearing in a reputable journal and written by researchers with impeccable credentials. Yet the paper received not a single media reference. What did receive coverage was a piece of research arriving at nearly opposite conclusions - an article suggesting that the earlier onset of seasons confirmed global warming predictions which was featured prominently in the *New York Times* ("Greener Green Belt Bears Witness to Warming Trend," April 22, 1997) and the *Washington Post* ("Spring Sprouting Earlier... Climate Report... Heats Up Debate Over Global Warming" April 17, 1997). Interestingly, even this research, by Ranga Myneni, appearing in *Nature*, presents an anomaly in that northern latitudes are said to be 10% greener, while the increase in atmospheric carbon dioxide, presumably the stimulus to the growth, was observed to have increased by only 4%.

Another interesting case involves research on satellite temperature measurements by James W. Hurrell and Kevin E. Trenberth, which appeared in *Nature* (March 13, 1997). Since satellite data are often cited by sceptics to show the absence of conclusiveness on warming, journalists had good grounds to be interested. The story led to headlines such as, "New Analysis Fans

Debate Over Global Warming Data; Sceptics Challenged by Recalculation of Satellite Readings" (*Washington Post* March 13, 1997) and "Satellite Cooling Data Disputed" (Boston Globe), where Hurrell is quoted as saying that "the satellite data have been misused... to make it appear there is no global warming" by sceptics.

But specific refutations of the Hurrell/Trenberth recalculations offered at a meteorological society meeting and presented in Washington at the Marshall Institute by University of Alabama satellite researcher John Christy, the effect of which are to sustain the validity of data showing an upper-atmosphere cooling over the last 17 years, was not covered by any major media (Christy is allowed to comment on the Hurrell/Trenberth thesis in some news accounts of their research). Hence, there was a clear asymmetry of coverage, and rather than a quest for 'balance,' journalists seemed to be attuned to only one kind of story. So embedded now is the Trenberth/Hurrell argument that Eugene Linden of Time magazine uses it in public forums to dismiss anyone who mentions satellite data, apparently unaware that Christy and others have rebutted the argument. Even science that is treated negatively by prominent climatologists can receive positive media attention if the 'take' is right. For instance, Robert Kaufmann of the Center for Energy and Environmental Studies at Boston University and David Stern of Australian National University published an article in *Nature* (July 3, 1997) that NCAR's Tom Wigley dismissed as "a simplification of what has been done.... I'm totally underwhelmed by their results." Nevertheless, the Associated Press reported the research under the headline, "Study: Humans Cause Global Warming."

In addition to science stories about the status of warming claims, journalists seem to operate selectively when confronted by stories about the impact of warming on human affairs. And the story line is predictable – disaster prevails over other scenarios. For instance, on May 22, 1997, researchers Roger Pielke of the National Center for Atmospheric Research (NCAR) and Christopher Landsea of the National Oceanic and Atmospheric Administration (NOAA) presented a paper at the American Meteorological Society Conference on Hurricanes and Tropical Meteorology entitled "Normalized Hurricane Damages in the United States: 1925–1995." The principle finding was that, despite "sources from the U.S. Senate to *Newsweek* magazine hav[ing] linked global warming to the past decade's rise in hurricane damages... most Atlantic hurricane seasons since 1970 have seen tropical cyclones occurring at a less frequent rate than the century-long average."

The reason for increased insurance pay-outs? Pielke and Landsea conclude it is "the continued flocking of Americans to vulnerable coastal locations... inflation... [and] increase in material wealth held by the average household." Though the paper was summarised in the science news postings available to environmental journalists, it made no news.

Instead, just three days later on May 25, 1997, Ross Gelbspan wrote in the *Washington Post* that "For the past few years, the ravages of the changing climate have been sending shock waves through the executive suites of international insurance companies.... In just the five years between 1990 and 1995, hurricanes, cyclones and floods across the globe have cost more than $30 billion a year."

The Gelbspan piece was followed two weeks later in the *New York Times* by a report (June 3, 1997) from William K. Stevens headlined "Storm Warnings: Bigger Hurricanes and More Of Them." The story reported on predictions from some climatologists of what may happen were the summer of 1997 to experience more hurricanes than normal, and were they to be of greater magnitude. Thus, an actual analysis of the existing meteorological record was displaced by a piece about speculative disaster in the future. Stevens followed on June 21 in the *New York Times* with a further piece the title of which is even more alarming: "El Niño Is Back, Scientist Says, With Threat of Global Havoc." Again, the story is based not on actual conditions or damages but on predictions of El Niño's potential future strength and its potential impact.

An equally striking juxtaposition featuring Ross Gelbspan occurred in the *Washington Post*, May 25, 1997 (so significant, apparently, that it was repeated verbatim in the *Sacramento Bee*, July 13, 1997). Gelbspan editorialised, "In January 1995, a vast section of the ice the size of Rhode Island broke off the Larsen ice shelf in Antarctica... it was one of the most spectacular and nightmarish manifestations yet of the ominous changes occurring on the planet. Two months later, a second shelf collapsed, leaving only a plume of fragments in the Weddell Sea as evidence of its 20,000 year existence. Scientists had predicted as early as the 1970s that the melting of Antarctica's ice shelves would signal the accelerated heating of the planet. They were not wrong... The Antarctic ice thaw may be the most dramatic evidence of global warming." Gelbspan, of course, is responsible for the positively breathtaking claim in the *Minneapolis Star-Tribune* (later corrected) that "Antarctica has warmed 20 degrees in the last 20 years."

None of the papers carrying Gelbspan's alarm, however, noted that, according to the National Science Foundation's Amundsen-Scott South Pole Station, "The South Pole has been experiencing the coldest weather since record keeping began 40 years ago... the average South Pole temperature during July was minus 86.8°F, breaking the previous record of 83.7," (a piece of information relayed only by Malcolm Browne in a *New York Times* Science Watch column).

More significantly, every newspaper but the *Washington Post* (which provided a Science Notebook comment on the issue) completely ignored pertinent research on the Antarctic ice sheet that made the cover story of *Nature* (July 31, 1997). "Will global warming melt the big Antarctic ice shelves? On the contrary, a study shows that moderate warming might actually thicken them.... The findings suggest that moderate climate warming would bring cooler waters in contact with the ice shelf and so cause it to thicken. Such a counter-intuitive result highlights the complexity of the ocean-atmosphere-cryosphere system." The article by K. W. Nichols, of the British Antarctic Survey, concludes, "the response of the ice shelf to a warming of the climate will be for it to thicken, reinforcing rather than threatening its longevity."

Some research, if it supports warming conclusions, is so compelling that its arguments can even be recycled after a decent interval – in this next case, 16 years – and still make big news. On September 4, 1997, Curt Suplee of the *Washington Post* reported a story from *Nature* of the same day arguing that the amount of sea ice surrounding the Antarctic region may have shrunk as much as 25%. Researcher William K. de la Mare examined whaling records dating back nearly 60 years to infer changes in the approximate extent of the sea ice, using recordings of the location of each whale catch kept since 1931, the longitude and latitude of which usually occurred within 6 to 22 miles of the ice edge, hence providing a "surrogate measure of sea ice extent."

But a search of science news shows that a remarkably comparable story had already run in the *New York Times* – the date?– October 19, 1981. With a headline of "Evidence is Found of Warming Trend," Robert Reinhold reports "new evidence that supports the theory that carbon dioxide pollution is causing a potentially dangerous warming of the earth's climate has been detected by scientists at Columbia University."

The study by George J. Kukla and Joyce E. Gavin appeared in the October 30, 1981 issue of *Science* (embargo-jumping was a problem in those days), and measured changes in the Antarctic ice pack by comparing "recent satellite photographs of the extent of the ice pack with...whaling ship reports from 1929 to 1938. They found that the typical summer ice pack had decreased about 35%" (taking the percentage change from both stories, it would appear that the big news should have been "Antarctic ice sheet recovers 10% from earlier shrinkage").

To understand the media's engagement with the story of global climate change, we need to recognise certain general features of modern media. First, the question of coverage generates a subsidiary question of whether the coverage of global warming is different in kind from the coverage of all other stories, or even other science stories. In general, what one finds is that certain types of science stories, of which global warming is one, get treated in approximately the same manner by the mainstream press, while the majority of science stories do not.

For example, research involving air or water pollution, endocrine disrupters, mad cow disease, silicone gel implants, deformed frogs, and food safety are very often portrayed in the media in a manner very comparable with climate change issues. But other science stories do not, such as, for example, those involving chloride-ion transport at the cell surface.

What are the characteristics of stories that receive a special treatment? In general, they claim an urgent threat to health or well-being, they reinforce the need for regulatory action or increased government intervention in human activities, and they are perceived to favour one faction in partisan political disputes.

Most importantly, they are stories that acquire symbolic value over and above their scientific substance. That is, one's stance with respect to a particular subject, certain or uncertain, committed to action or qualified by reservations, becomes a referendum regarding one's stance in some other domain, such as the political or the compassionate. To accept or reject a bit of science, then, becomes a signal of what kind of person you are, and of whether your motives are pure or crass.

Hence, the common manoeuvre on the part of antagonists is to resort to the ad hominem. Ross Gelbspan's dismissals of climate sceptics are well known, but sometimes researchers and not just journalist advocates join in. Ben Santer of Lawrence

13

Livermore claimed that his integrity as a scientist was in question after a *Wall Street Journal* piece criticised his role in producing the IPCC document. On the other hand, Kevin Trenberth, author of a study dismissing satellite data, has characterised sceptic Pat Michaels as being "similar to a scientist working for a tobacco company who found there was no link between smoking and cancer." Moreover, he was said to have published "only a couple of papers in the last five years... and they were not key papers."

Journalists, following the pattern of rational ignorance, will often depend upon the outcome of a previous science story as a template or emblematic episode that they bring wholesale to a new and complex story. Sometimes this template is treated as broadly instructive about the likely shape of new stories that they encounter. For many greenhouse sceptics, for instance, the Alar story provides a cautionary model of how a spurious alarm was driven by weak science harnessed to an effective media campaign. Alar, a pesticide, was alleged (falsely, it was later shown) to be a dangerous carcinogen at low doses. Its prohibition led to the loss of thousands of jobs. The 'lesson' these sceptics derive is that global climate change should likewise be scrutinised sceptically, especially once they sense that political and media pressure appears to be pushing for action that may prove to be precipitous.

In contrast, journalist Eugene Linden of *Time* magazine, who is receptive to global warming stories, does not rely on the Alar model. Instead, Linden explained that he understands global warming by analogy with his experience of the ozone issue. As he stated in a public forum at the Smithsonian Institution, the ozone debate showed that had journalists listened to people such as Andrew Molina and Sherwood Rowlands of the University of California at Irvine (subsequent Nobel laureates for their work on atmospheric chemistry which in 1974 had proposed the theoretical possibility of ozone damage), "we could have stopped ozone depletion in the late 70s, but the political climate changed and President Ronald Reagan allowed Dupont to obfuscate and delay and raise doubts and point out uncertainties. Hence, that is how we should see the current global climate debate... farsighted scientists being hindered by interested industry apologists."

Journalists are certainly subject to pressure, but this does not always, as Linden has it, derive from industry sources. For instance, Boyce Rensberger of the *Washington Post* states that the reaction of environmental activists to his 1992 coverage of global warming issues was to apply pressure on him to mirror their views more closely. Rensberger stated that the response of 'organised environmentalism' to his pieces was for Michael Oppenheimer of the Environmental Defense Fund to "call a meeting with him to discuss his coverage." According to Rensberger, the problem was not related to charges of factual errors, but rather that the 'tone' of the pieces had not conveyed sufficient alarm.

Over time, the pressure does seem to have its intended effect, visible when even relatively benign or ambiguous research that does not necessarily advance warming alarm will be 'mined' for an interpretation that does. For example, the *Wall Street Journal's* John Fialka forwarded the Environmental Defense Fund's projection of the impact of climate change on New Hampshire, showing how warming trends could damage the state's tourism industry, "driving the sugar maple farther north.... [and] making autumn coloration more gradual and less attractive."

Another example of a journalist apparently 'spun' by those who can provide alarming insights from most any climate development would be Richard Monastersky of *Science News*. His article "Global Warming Lurks Principally at Night" (July 19, 1997) reported research that was not inherently frightening; most of the effects of warming would be confined to slight temperature increases at night, rather than elevating daytime maximums. But Monastersky found an interpretation that conveyed danger by interviewing the right commentator: "Scientists who study climate and agriculture, however, point out that warmer nights can stimulate the growth of harmful insects and weeds. They can also reduce yields by spurring plants to burn energy faster at night. Moreover, such climate change further limits the places where farmers can plant winter wheat, which requires cold temperatures, says Cynthia Rosenzweig of NASA's Goddard Institute for Space Studies in New York."

Our commonplace assumption that the news functions as a window on the world, objectively transmitting images from reality into headlines, is regularly belied by any careful examination of events and their subsequent treatment. Rather than a purely translucent medium passing events through to the reader, news appears to operate more as a combination of filter and prism.That is, selection is always operating in news coverage, picking out certain events in the world and ignoring others; the ones selected for transmission are always subject to some sort of alteration, the events being cut and shaped by a variety of considerations until they fit.

Hence, news is an active process of construction as well as a passive medium of transport. Moreover, while we may naïvely expect the news to be 'newsworthy,' that is, the presentation of something novel and significant, we should recognise that aspect as only one dimension of what makes news worthy of 'selection' and transmission.

The other aspect has more in common with a mythos, or a steady reiteration and validation that the world is just exactly as we have always thought it should be, and that today's news is best when it re-confirms us in our most deep-seated beliefs about the way things really are.

Many media analysts speak of this second aspect, the mythos dimension, by using terms like cultural template, scenario, or controlling narrative. That is, we should conceive of our cultural world as composed of certain deeply embedded narrative shapes and stories, perennial tales and accounts with recognisable plot lines and character evaluations, with various morals that express our value commitments.

A moral world filled with heroes and villains, dangers and triumphs, greed and disinterested heroism, alarms and escapes, dastardly cover-ups by the powerful and heroic unmaskings, and in general plucky underdogs successfully fighting city hall, is one embedded in the American landscape. Journalists, often refugees of humanities training in college, are primed to expect such narratives by Ibsen's Dr. Stockman in *Enemy of the People*, or Eugene O'Neill's Hickey in *The Ice Man Cometh*, Arthur Miller's stalwart in *The Crucible*, or history's examples such as Galileo and the church. News that alerts us to dangers, thereby demanding our attention, and that can be shaped so as to confirm the moral world, thereby commanding our affirmation, is a sure-fire hit (let us not forget the characterisation of the journalist's calling by one of Washington's most important publishers as being 'to right society's wrongs').

Science stories that can be constructed in one of these template shapes become enduring and appealing, helping us to hold a moral referendum on a variety of seemingly unrelated issues by virtue of the stance we take on the scientific question. In addition to specific templates brought to stories from the experience of previous scientific episodes, reporters also work with certain broad cultural themes. For instance, the controlling narrative that often catches reporters' interest is to pitch a story involving bought lackeys confronted by white knights of the public interest. Increasingly, rather than the cogency of one's argument, the number of publications, prestige of appointments held, political leanings, and especially, funding sources, become the chits in the battle of legitimacy. Reporters, practising their rational ignorance, learn to treat these signs as convenient substitutes for the task of delving into arcane science.

A reporter for the *Arizona Republic* sums up this perspective by quoting with approval Carl Sagan, who advised all journalists to ask: "In whose interest is it to minimise these concerns? The answer is there is an industry that would be severely affected." Hence, the reporter concludes, greenhouse critics like Arizona's own Dr. Robert Balling "should continue to be heard, but they should not counterbalance the overwhelming consensus of scientific opinion."

Other narrative templates involve plucky underdogs confronting massive corporate cover-ups, or the use of vivid, personal, and image-laden writing. So, Ross Gelbspan's controlling narrative in his Harper's piece opens with a vivid scene of personal conflagration, hitched to implication of a deliberate cover-up of the truth: "After my lawn had burned away to straw last summer.... I wondered how long we can go on pretending that nothing is amiss with the world's weather."

Anything but shy, Gelbspan raises the stakes somewhat in his March 19, 1995 *Washington Post* piece written with Harvard University Public Health specialist Epstein; he is no longer worried just about his lawn but the whole of humanity; "Should we fear global plague? Yes Disease is the Deadliest Threat of Rising Temperatures."

A more important question may be not why certain stories of alarm get published; that is very likely to be simply the natural response of the medium. Rather, what must be accounted for is why some stories are ignored, even studiously, given what we hear the press say about itself. In particular, we must ask why one very significant story, with all the right wrappings and colourful presentations, went unchomped – I speak of Richard Kerr's *Science* piece detailing the uncertainties in climate modelling. Until his arguments were insistently pushed by some think tanks, the entire article went unremarked by the mainstream press. Part of the answer why journalists ignored the article is that the uncertainty stressed by the piece leaves them checked: what to do for tomorrow's lead? The piece is of no more value to journalists than would be a weather report that consisted of 'uncertain today, uncertain tomorrow, and our five-day forecast is for continued uncertainty.'

What we ultimately have to account for is how a story such as Richard Kerr's now famous piece in *Science* could have ended so prophetically. "The last thing he and his colleagues' want is a rash of headlines saying the threat is over," concluded Kerr, speaking of Gerald North of Texas A & M. And no headlines is exactly what North got.

References

Allen, S (1997) 'Are skeptics winning debate on warming? Tiny minority has undue influence, book says.' *Boston Globe'* April 28.

Chandler, D. L. (1997) 'Satellite cooling data disputed' *Boston Globe*, March 13.

Crenson, M. (1997) 'Ecologists seeing signs of climate change, but is it humans' fault?' *The Associated Press,* July 7.

de la Mare, W. K. (1997) 'Abrupt mid-twentieth century decline in Antarctic sea-ice extent from whaling records' *Nature,* **389**, pp. 57-58, September 4.

Drent, R. (1996) 'Scientist's theories too simple' *The Sunday Star-Times* (Auckland), May 12.

Gelbspan, R (1997) 'The Heat is On: the high stakes battle over Earth's threatened climate', New York: Addison-Wesley Publishing Company, p34.

Gelbspan, R (1997) 'Hot air, cold truth: why do we pay attention to greenhouse skeptics? *The Washington Post*, May 25.

Geophysical Research Letters, (1996) **22**(10), May 15.

Goodridge, J. D. (1996) 'Comments on "Regional simulations of greenhouse warming including natural variability' *Bulletin of the American Meteorological Society,* **77**, pp1588-89.

Hotz, R. L. (1996) 'Butterflies head north to beat rising heat' *Los Angeles Times* August 29.

Hurrell, J. W. and Trenberth, K. E. (1997) 'Spurious trends in satellite MSU temperatures from merging different satellite records' *Nature* **386**; pp 164-167, March 13.

Kaufmann, R. K. and Stern, D. I. (1997) 'Evidence for human influence on climate from hemispheric temperature relations' *Nature* **388**; pp 39-44, July 3.

Kerr, R. A. (1997) 'Greenhouse forecasting is still cloudy' *Science,* **276,** pp 1040-1042, May 16.

Linden, E. (1997) 'Global warming: how journalism covers the question' *Global Warming: Understanding the Forecast* A speech delivered at the National Museum of Natural History, July 22.

Monastersky, R. (1997) 'Global warming lurks principally at night' *Science News* **152** p 38, July 19.

Myneni, R. B. (1997) 'Increased plant growth in the northern latitudes from 1981-1991' *Nature* **396;** p 698, April 17.

Nicholls, K. W. (1997) 'Predicted reduction in basal melt rates of an Antarctic ice shelf in a warmer climate' *Nature*, **388** pp 460-461, July 31.

Parmesan, C. (1996) 'Climate and species' range' *Nature*, **382**, August 29, pp 765-766.

Reinhold. R. (1981) 'Evidence is found of warming trend' *New York Times* October 19.

Rensberger, B. (1997) 'Global warming: how journalism covers the question' *Global Warming: Understanding the Forecast* A speech delivered at the National Museum of Natural History, July 22.

Stevens, W. K. (1996) 'Western butterfly shifting north as global climate warms' *New York Times,* September 3.

Stevens, W. K. (1997) 'Greener green belt bears witness to warming trend' *New York Times,* April 22.

Toner, M (1996) 'Butterfly exodus: global warming may be pushing species northward' *Atlanta Constitution* August 29.

Warrick, J. (1997) 'Spring sprouting earlier...' *The Washington Post,* April 17.

Wilson, S. (1995) 'Can we take the chance global warming is a sham?' *Arizona Republic,* November 24.

David Wyndham Murray

David Murray was born in Hollywood, California. B.S. Philosophy and Anthropology, Brigham Young University, M.A., Ph.D. University of Chicago, in Social and Cultural Anthropology. Taught at Connecticut College, Brown University, and Brandeis University. Currently Director of Research, the Statistical Assessment Service (STATS), a non-profit organisation dedicated to improving media coverage of scientific and statistical information. He is also Adjunct Professor, Graduate Institute of Public Policy, Georgetown University.

Section I

Method, Applied Science and Policy

The State of Climate Change Science

Dr. Roy W. Spencer
Senior Scientist
NASA

Global Warming: Science or Politics?

Within the science of global warming it is often difficult to separate what the data show from what the scientists want the data to show. In a sense, it is usually not the facts that are in question, but the interpretation of those facts. Politics, world views, and the pressure to publish and secure research funding all act to compromise scientific objectivity. Add to these complications the cost of being wrong on such an important issue, and we have a scientific problem with which science has a difficult time dealing. The theory of global warming will probably never be validated or falsified since we cannot put the Earth in a laboratory to run experiments on it. About all we can hope for is that sufficient measurements can be accumulated in support and in opposition to the theory to eventually make some generalized statements reflecting our uncertainty of the existence and magnitude of global warming.

Despite this uncertainty, after the 1995 Second Assessment of the IPCC there were widespread claims that over 2,000 of the world's climate scientists had come to a "consensus" on the threat of global warming. The IPCC statement that "the balance of evidence suggests that there is a discernible human influence on global climate" seems potent at first sight, but its language is artfully hedged with words such as "balance", "suggests", and "discernible". There is evidence to suggest that this statement was pushed to help accomplish the political agendas of those in control of the IPCC process, and in particular to further the progress of the Framework Convention on Climate Change. That there was political pressure from the U.S. State Department to arrive at a pro-global warming stance in the 1995 IPCC report is now indisputable. This has led some scientists to the conclusion that the U.N. is corrupting the scientific process. Yet we should not be surprised to find a political body pushing for answers to a question of such great potential importance to humanity.

The climate system is immensely complex. Unfortunately, it is in the human nature of scientists to be most sure of the problems we know the least about. Typically, the more we learn about a problem, the less we find we really understand. The fact that the magnitude of global warming projections has steadily been revised downward over the last ten years is some evidence for this. Also, a scientist's faith in his scientific position on an issue will be strengthened if he believes there is little risk if he is wrong. Indeed, if there was a solution to the global warming threat which cost nothing to implement, I would be willing to say there is sufficient evidence in favour of global warming to go ahead and implement that solution. Thus, we also have the scientist's understanding of economics influencing his scientific opinions.

Remaining Uncertainties: Water Vapour

I believe that there is still great uncertainty about the climate system response to increasing levels of greenhouse gases. While many IPCC scientists study the complexities of the highly uncertain effects of aerosols and clouds (which are no doubt legitimate problems to study), they have long ago stopped questioning the largest source of global warming in general circulation models (GCMs): positive water vapour feedback (Zhang et al., 1994). This is the supposed process whereby a small amount of warming induced by increasing CO_2 leads to increases in the water vapour content of the atmosphere. Since water vapour is by far the most important greenhouse gas in the atmosphere, this causes further warming, which causes further moistening, and thus a positive feedback cycle. While it is true that warmer air tends to be moister near the Earth's surface, it is much less certain whether this is the case higher in the atmosphere, where the processes controlling the water vapour distribution are much more complex and not well handled by GCMs. The lower the humidity in this 'free-tropospheric' region, the more important those processes become due to the great efficiency with which dry air radiates infrared energy to outer space (Lindzen, 1995).

New measurements of the warmest part of the Earth, the tropics, have revealed that the relative humidity is exceedingly low over the vast oceanic deserts called the subtropical high pressure zones (Spencer and Braswell, 1997). This dry air overlays very moist air in the layer closest to the surface, called the boundary layer. It is important to understand how these dry areas are maintained, and especially how they respond to anomalous warmth in the tropics, in order to validate positive water vapour feedback in GCMs (Pierrehumbert, 1995; Sun and Lindzen, 1993). Because the processes controlling the dryness of these regions are related to rain cloud microphysics, it is the opinion of a few scientists that we might never be able to adequately represent these processes in GCMs (Renno et al., 1994).

Global Temperatures: Warming or Cooling?

Sometimes the facts themselves are open to debate, let alone their interpretation. The satellite record of global lower tropospheric temperatures (Spencer and Christy, 1992) have revealed a slight cooling trend of -0.10°C/decade in the tropics since the satellite record began in 1979. This has been found to be at variance with sea water temperatures measured by scattered ships and buoys, which show a warming trend of about the same magnitude over the same period (Hurrell and Trenberth, 1997). Such a disagreement appears to the public as if scientists cannot agree on how global temperatures have varied in the past, and to some extent this is true. One possibility is that both are correct, since the processes controlling the two separate phenomena are not perfectly coupled. While Hurrell and Trenberth utilized a GCM to argue that the two trends should be nearly the same, until now science has never had the data to validate whether tropospheric temperatures should track sea water temperatures over two decades to the level of 0.2°C. Again, the microphysics of rain clouds are important to this problem, and the rain physics in GCMs are known to be suspect. This issue will continue to be debated in the scientific literature (Christy et al., 1997).

Global Temperatures and The Second Law

What we do know for sure is that weather systems are always acting to rid the Earth of excess heat. This is an example of the Second Law of Thermodynamics, that energy will flow from areas with higher concentrations to those with lower concentrations. This law is so fundamental that we might consider this to be weather systems' most important role in the climate system. Excess solar heating in the tropics, or over certain sub-regions, is continually causing the atmosphere to overturn convectively, dumping heat high in the atmosphere where the excess energy can radiate out to space more efficiently. Much of this heat is removed from the surface through the evaporation of water. Low and high pressure areas, and their wind systems, transport heat from areas of temperature excess to regions of temperature deficit. The whole process not only helps to cool the warm regions, but also helps to warm the polar regions. This 'big picture' is not often discussed because climate scientists are usually caught up in the study of a

25

specific process, for example the warming or cooling effects of a certain type of cloud. This focus on details is necessary because each process is so complex that we have time in our careers thoroughly to understand only a small part of the whole system, sometimes missing the wood for the trees. Despite the complexity of the individual processes which make up the totality of the climate system, we know from the Second Law that all of these myriad processes are tied together to ultimately achieve one goal: the rejection of excess heat.

While I would not argue that all of the additional heat that is being trapped by increasing greenhouse gas concentrations will be rejected fast enough to prevent any global warming whatsoever, I do believe that GCMs predictions of global warming will only be tenable when all the negative feedbacks in the climate system are adequately represented. These are the processes which cause the climate system to return to a state of balance when it is perturbed. That GCMs typically do not have enough of these processes is evidenced by their tendency to drift toward unrealistically warm or cold states. Even for those models that are now adjusted to not drift, it is likely that the adjustments made are not the correct ones to realistically stabilise the model. As an example of the stability of the climate system, satellites often reveal a sudden warming of the tropical troposphere by an amount equivalent to 100 years of global warming in only two weeks. However, in these cases, the system rapidly returns to a normal state, often overshooting into an unusually cool state, only to begin a warming phase again. Thus, tropical temperatures act like a weight hanging from a coiled spring, constantly oscillating about a mean state. Why don't these sudden warmings cause positive water vapour feedback, and push the climate system warmer? Probably because a variety of negative feedbacks act to keep the system in check.

How Sensitive is the Climate System?

Some scientists believe that the non-linear (or chaotic) nature of the components of the climate system can cause a sudden shift into a new state of equilibrium, disrupting regional weather patterns after decades or centuries of apparent stability. There is some small amount evidence to support this view. The El Niño/Southern Oscillation, which has a time scale of several years, seems to behave in this manner. However, it is quite a leap of faith to believe that human influence can result in a sudden shift in climate. I am often amazed at the lengths to which scientists will carry the 'butterfly effect' analogy: that the wings of a butterfly in

Japan can make the difference between a storm developing or not in the United States. If a butterfly can do this, then how much more might we expect the climate system to push itself into new states of equilibrium? For instance, the 1991 eruption of Mount Pinatubo in the Philippines was estimated to reduce the amount of sunlight entering the troposphere by 2-4%. Hurricanes and super-typhoons are dramatic events, releasing amounts of energy far greater than the world's nuclear arsenals. Why do we not worry that these events will disrupt the climate system as well?

The Future of Global Warming Knowledge

The coming years will continue to see improvements in our understanding of how the climate system operates, which will be translated into improvements in GCMs. However, as mentioned above, these will no doubt be accompanied by new questions which will arise as a result of that research. The myriad and complex roles of water in the climate system, e.g. water vapour, clouds, rainfall, snow and sea ice, and the oceanic circulation, will continue to amaze scientists through its ability to maintain an equitable temperature on Earth. The non-linear ways in which many water processes interact will continue to make them particularly difficult to understand and quantify. As a result, I predict that policy decisions regarding climate change issues will always have to be made with great uncertainty, no matter what may be the 'consensus' of the research community.

References

Christy, J. R., R.W. Spencer, and W. D. Braswell, 1997: Satellites are quite accurate. Submitted to *Nature*.

Hurrell, J. W., and K.E. Trenberth, 1997:Spurious trends in the satellite MSU temperature record arising from merging different satellite records. *Nature*, 386, 164-167.

Intergovernmental Panel on Climate Change, 1995: Climate Change 1995: The Second IPCC Assessment. Cambridge University Press.

Lindzen, R.S., 1995: The importance and *Nature* of the water vapour budget in *Nature* and models. In Climate Sensitivity to Radiative Perturbations: Physical Mechanisms and their Validation, NATO ASI Series 1: Global Environmental Change, 34, H. Le Treut (editor), Springer-Verlag, Heidelberg.

Pierrehumbert, R.T., 1995: Thermostats, radiator fins, and the local runaway greenhouse. *J. Atmos. Sci.*, 52, 1784-1806.

Renno, N. O., K. A. Emanuel, and P. H. Stone, 1994: Radiative-convective model with an explicit hydrologic cycle 1. Formulation and sensitivity to model parameters. *J. Geophys. Res.*, 99, 14,429-14,441.

Spencer, R.W., and W. D. Braswell, 1997: How dry is the tropical free troposphere? Implications for global warming theory. *Bull. Amer. Meteor. Soc*, June.

Spencer, R.W., and J. R. Christy, 1992: Precision and radiosonde validation of satellite gridpoint temperature anomalies, Part II: A tropospheric retrieval and trends during 1979-90. *J. Climate*, 5, 858-866.

Sun, D.-Z. and R.S. Lindzen, 1993: Distribution of tropical tropospheric water vapour. *J. Atmos. Sci.*, 50, 1643-1660.

Zhang, M.H., J.J. Hack, J.T. Kiehl, and R. D. Cess, 1994: Diagnostic study of climate feedback processes in atmospheric general circulation models. *J. Geophys. Res.*, 99, 5525-5537.

Roy W. Spencer

Dr. Roy W. Spencer is Senior Scientist for Climate Studies at NASA's Marshall Space Flight Center, in Huntsville, Alabama. He leads a research effort to utilise satellite data to understand better how the climate system functions, and to monitor the Earth for signs of global warming. These satellite measurements include temperature, water vapour, and precipitation estimates from a variety of satellite-based sensors. He is co-developer of the only method of precision monitoring of global temperature variations with satellites. Dr. Spencer is also the U.S. Science Team leader for the Advanced Microwave Scanning Radiometer, which will fly on NASA's PM-1 satellite in late 2000 as part of NASA's Mission to Planet Earth. He is the recipient of NASA's Exceptional Scientific Achievement medal, and received the American Meteorological Society's 1996 Special Award for his temperature monitoring work.

The Role of Remote Sensing in Climate Monitoring

Robin Vaughan
University of Dundee,
Dundee
UK

Summary

Remote sensing, or Earth observation from satellites and aircraft, is a recent innovation which would seem ideally suited to the large scale, periodic monitoring of the world's environment and climate. By outlining the mechanisms by which such observations are made, the natural constraints on such observations, and the problems associated with obtaining reliable data and in interpreting it, some of its limitations for global climate monitoring are demonstrated. Only when such limitations are fully appreciated can climatologists and other scientists make intelligent use of remote sensing as a source of data to be integrated with those data from other sources.

Introduction

Remote sensing is a technology by which the surface of the Earth may be observed from a satellite or aircraft. This is perhaps a rather narrow definition for a technique which has many similarities to astronomy, which can be used to study the atmosphere and can also be carried out from other platforms, and perhaps the more recent title 'earth observation' is more apt, particularly in the present context, but I want to examine that first definition closely in order to try to give some indication of the usefulness and limitations of the technology for climate monitoring.

Let us begin by quoting from an official briefing about the Centre for Earth Observation (CEO – an EU project set up to try to increase the usage of remotely-sensed data and hence to justify expenditure in the European Space Agency's programmes). 'Twenty years ago, the potential for Earth Observation (EO) seemed boundless... With the outstanding exception of weather prediction, EO has not lived up to optimistic expectations. Why has this been so? Why is it that there are many disgruntled users around the world? Surely all the data available to us through the new technologies of satellites and computers must, almost by definition, be 'useful'? Again, we need to examine these statements very carefully before drawing any conclusions.

It is worth digressing to consider why it is that there should be disgruntled users. From the mid-1970s onward, remote sensing was heavily oversold, partly by technological enthusiasts in research institutes but mainly by providers of data, hardware and software. Developing countries were sold elaborate systems which were difficult to operate and maintain, and which quickly became obsolete. Users with operational requirements were persuaded to invest time and money in applications projects which could not succeed because there was no promise of continuity of data supply. Only the defence and meteorological communities had enough resources and political muscle to ensure supply of adequate operational data streams. The situation is changing, but improvement is slow. Recent arrivals such as computer workstations, powerful PCs and the Internet have revolutionised the affordability and accessibility of the means of manipulating data. Promised investment in the space sector should increase the amount of data available. But it is not data that the end user requires, but useful information, and therein lies the rub! We risk being drowned in a sea of data, but without the means of handling it, without the means of extracting the information and without the means of using that information we may as well spend that money on more useful ways of improving the human lot.

Defining the technique

Let us go back and examine our working definition of remote sensing. It is a technology, not a science in itself, rather a source of data – and just one source of data. Those data need to be interpreted and analysed by experts and used in conjunction with data from other sources. Remote sensing rarely takes the place of other techniques, but can be used, for example, to extrapolate in situ measurements over large areas or over extended time periods. The data received at the satellite is a measure of the amount of radiation in a certain waveband that emanates from a certain portion of the Earth's surface below and that has travelled through, and hence interacted with, the atmosphere through which it has passed. Relating that measured quantity to the physical parameters of the area that emitted or reflected it is by no means simple. It is possible, using sophisticated mathematical modelling, to obtain an absolute measure of temperature from space, but very few other

31

quantities can actually be measured in absolute terms. That is where other sources of data, such as ground-based measurements, are required, for calibration or identification purposes.

The next significant word in the definition is surface. To all intents and purposes the only information one can gather from space is about the surface of the Earth. Microwaves (radar) can penetrate a few centimetres or metres of dry material, such as the sand in the desert, and blue light will penetrate clear water and show up features some metres underwater, but these are unusual situations. Blue light is rarely made use of in remote sensing because it is greatly scattered by the atmosphere, and solid ground is often wet or covered with vegetation which obscures the surface you want to look at. Sea-surface temperatures measured remotely really do relate only to the surface. There can be a temperature gradient of as much as several degrees over the top few millimetres of the water and so such temperatures measured from space may not reflect the bulk water temperature which are those usually measured in situ. The oceans themselves are also very deep in places, are highly mobile and store and transport enormous quantities of energy. They play a hugely significant role in the Earth's energy balance and hence in its climate and yet we can only monitor the surface. Having said that, though, it is the surface at which the oceans interact with the atmosphere and energy is exchanged across this surface, so such measurements can be useful.

Next, what do we mean by the word 'observe'? As mentioned earlier, the detector on board the satellite (or aircraft, of course) receives and responds to the electromagnetic radiation falling on it. This radiation may have originated on the Sun, travelled through space and, more importantly, the atmosphere, been reflected from the surface of the Earth and travelled yet further through the atmosphere, interacting with the molecules of gases, aerosols, dust etc. on the way. It is then focused onto a detector, probably having passed through a prism or grating to separate out the different wavebands ('colours' in the visible part of the spectrum, but the Sun also emits radiation outside the visible, in the ultraviolet and infrared). The Earth itself may be the source of thermal electromagnetic radiation (heat) and microwaves, but microwaves are usually generated on board the satellite and it is the reflected beam which is detected. Modern detectors usually employ a scanning mechanism to build up an image. Unlike in a camera (which produces an instantaneous 'picture' of the whole field of view), small areas of ground are successively 'observed' as the scanner mirror rotates, and the total energy from that area is recorded by the detector. Hence no particular detail within this area can be resolved, only the 'average' value of the radiation. As the mirror rotates, and as the platform moves forward, a mosaic of such responses is measured and an 'image' of the ground is built up, line by line. The image therefore consists of 'tiles' or 'picture elements' (pixels), each corresponding to the relevant area of ground below. The size of these pixels may vary from about $10m^2$ to $1km^2$, depending on the particular satellite or scanner system being used, and this then limits the spatial resolution of the data since features smaller than this will just not show up. One reason for using a scanner rather than a camera is that the quantised data can be transmitted by radio back to Earth and, in digital form, can be processed on a computer. The Russians have had some success at returning high-resolution photographs from space, but the risks attached to catching the ejected film cassettes in large 'fishing nets' behind high-flying aircraft are rather great! It is clear, then, that the word 'observe' is perhaps to be interpreted broadly.

One therefore has to be very careful and not expect too much from the promises implied in the concept of remote sensing. What follows is an analysis of the technological limitations inherent in the remote sensing process.

Defining the problems

So far we have looked at how technological factors affect the ability to determine the spatial variability of features, and have hinted that there might also be problems associated with spectral variability – the fact that most surfaces respond differently to different wavelengths. White light consists of all colours between blue and red. Most surfaces reflect each component wavelength differently. This is fortunate because if they reflected all wavelengths equally we would not be able to distinguish between different surfaces and different objects and we would be for ever bumping into things! The ability to detect subtle variations in reflectivity at different wavelengths depends on the selectivity of the detecting instrument. Since each detector in a scanner detects only one band of wavelengths, the more detectors that are used and the closer they are spaced across the spectrum, the greater the variability which can be detected. But, as usual, technology places limitations on the extent to which this can be achieved. The narrower the bandwidth, the less energy it contains and therefore the less sensitive the detector will be. Sensitivity can be improved by collecting energy from a larger area, but of course this reduces the spatial resolution, or by spending a longer time looking at the smaller area. This latter can be achieved by using more modern components and different scanning techniques and has led to the development of so-called 'hyperspectral scanners'. But more wavebands means more data and this has to be transmitted back to Earth and stored and processed on a computer, stretching present technology to its limits. Different scanners, designed for different applications, may collect two or three broad bands or eight to ten narrow ones. So far, hyperspectral instruments have only been flown on aircraft when the data can be stored on board and processed at leisure.

Now what of the ability to make periodic observations? An advantage of using aircraft is that they can respond to demand. They can look at particular areas or features and follow their development as required. The spatial resolution, and often spectral resolution, of the instruments they carry can be far superior to those on satellites. Unfortunately the size of the area imaged is much smaller than from a satellite and so to cover an appreciable area would be both time consuming and very costly. The orbits of satellites, on the other hand, are predetermined and more or less immutable. The orbital period varies with height. In general terms, there are two classes of orbit. The first, the so-called geostationary orbit, is very high – about 36,000 km. A satellite in such an orbit will circle the Earth around the equator with a period of 24 hours – exactly the same as the period of rotation of the Earth. The satellite therefore appears to be stationary to an observer on the Earth (of course, if it really were stationary it would fall down!). This orbit is favoured by the communications industry because the satellite is always in the same position, making it easy to bounce radio signals off it using a simple, inexpensive fixed antenna. The second class of orbit is usually very much lower (only 700-800 km for the low Earth orbit environmental satellites) and passes more or less north-south, nearly over the poles, hence the name 'polar orbit'. The period of such an orbit is about 100 minutes, but if the orbit is offset by 10-20 degrees from the poles the orbit 'precesses'. This means that the Earth rotates underneath the satellite as it orbits and so each time it passes over the equator the Earth has moved on a bit. The track of the satellite therefore slowly moves around the equator, coming back to where it started after a predetermined number of orbits determined by the offset angle. The number of orbits chosen for this to happen is in turn determined by the width of the sub-satellite track which is imaged (the 'swath width') so that every part of the Earth's surface is imaged at some stage. Satellites such as NOAA, designed for meteorological use where the features are usually very large and swath widths of 3000-4000 km are imaged, pass overhead every twelve hours, whereas satellites such as Landsat and SPOT[1], designed for land resources mapping at high resolution, have a swath width of only a few hundred kilometres and so take between 16 and 27 days between overhead passes. Polar orbiting satellites also have to be tracked using large, expensive moveable antennae which can only receive signals while the satellite is in the line of sight of the receiving station. This limits the coverage from any particular place and means that a network of such stations around the world is required.

Again there is a trade-off to be made, this time between frequency of observation and spatial resolution. The scanner on the geostationary satellite is always looking at the same face of the Earth and can therefore collect images as frequently as is technologically possible – typically every half-hour. Meteosat, for example, images the whole of the Earth's disc from its vantage point over the equator at the Greenwich meridian, but at a spatial resolution of only 2.5 to 5 km (this variation is because of the distortion introduced by the curvature of the surface as you proceed from the centre point to the perimeter of the disc). The scanner on SPOT images at a spatial resolution of 10m but only once every 27 days (and that only if cloud free), that on Landsat at 30m resolution every 16 days and the one on NOAA at 1km resolution every 12 hours. Which is 'best' depends on your own particular field of application.

Problems of scaling

The compilation of a databank for environmental use is very complex. Not only are the data of different types (field data, satellite data, statistical data, census data, map data etc.) and in different formats (vector, statistical, tabular) but they also relate to different scales of measurement. Satellite images need to be geometrically registered and turned into temperature maps, land class maps, vegetation maps etc. before they can be combined

---

[1] NOAA is a meteorological satellite designed to look at clouds and atmospheric features over large areas but which change rapidly with time. Landsat and SPOT were designed for land applications where vegetational features may change seasonally or annually but where finer spatial detail is required.

with other datasets. The incompatibility of different data formats, classification methods, encoding routines etc., then have to be overcome, as do the problems of different kinds and scales of variables, incompatibility of hardware, and also the incompatibility of the 'hard' scientists and the social scientists who both have input to and require output from an 'environmental information system'.

One of the advantages of remotely sensed data is the snapshot synoptic view it gives. Previously, sea surface temperature maps and wind field plots were obtained by making a series of one-off measurements as ships travelled across the oceans. The problem with these types of measurement is that, not only are the measurements made only along busy shipping routes and in the more hospitable parts of the world, but that temperatures and winds change with time. Depicting time-varying measurements in a spatial fashion on a map is often meaningless, and a much better understanding of such phenomena as ocean currents has been obtained since the advent of satellite imagery. This illustrates a problem which is exercising the minds of many people, for example, hydrologists, at present. How can you incorporate disparate datasets into models? Continuous series of rainfall measurements are taken at a number of sampling points on the ground extending over several years. How does one correlate these with occasional regional-scale satellite measurements of precipitation? On the one hand you have small spatial scale and large temporal scale data and on the other hand infrequent data on a large spatial scale. This problem was alluded to a number of times in the previous volume in this series (ESEF, 1996), particularly with reference to global temperature measurements. Ingenious detective work has been done in trying to estimate trends in temperature from, for example, diary entries recording the date that blossoms appeared in China many hundreds of years ago, but the significant statement was that satellite measurements have indicated that there has been **no** increase in global temperatures over the last twenty years or so. Here we really are comparing like with like and not trying to make allowances for unknown variability factors.

Drowning in data

The National Climate Data Centre in America houses more than 200 terabytes of data (1 terabyte equals 10^{12} bytes) in forms that range from digital media to the paper logs recorded by Benjamin Franklin and Thomas Jefferson. There are half a million magnetic tapes, 200 million pages of information and 97,000 rolls of film. If all were placed end to end, they would go round the world eleven times. Data are now being collected at a rate of 55 gigabytes a day which is equivalent to about 18 million printed pages and NASA's planned 'Mission to Planet Earth' programme expects to generate up to one terabyte per day. Great steps are continually being made in increasing the capacity of storage media. A CD ROM can hold about 600 megabytes of data and a new laser read/write medium based on dye-polymer WORM (write once read many times) technology can hold one terabyte of data, equivalent to more than 4600 standard magnetic tape cartridges. But computing speeds will have to continue to increase at least at the present rate simply in order to handle such datastreams, let alone to be able to process and analyse the data in anything approaching real time. Present techniques for extracting information from data, merging it with other datasets and producing meaningful results are still painfully slow and laborious in many cases. Certainly advances are taking place rapidly, but not nearly as fast as the generation of data. Therefore analysis of the data is the bottleneck in information processing.

Defining the solution

The global warming scare has certainly stimulated activity. Quasi-autonomous bodies were set up, research was funded and NASA, for example, intends to launch dozens of satellites over the next few decades (the Earth Observing System – EOS) as part of the so-called 'Mission to Planet Earth', to study all manner of environmental parameters. EOS consists of a series of polar orbiting and low inclination satellites for long-term global observation of the land surface, biosphere, solid earth, atmosphere and oceans. In parallel with this will be other satellites operated by Europe and Japan, forming the comprehensive International Earth Observation System (IEOS). Other missions to measure the earth's radiation budget, albedo, solar radiation etc. are also included. But will this help to provide the solution? The executive summary of the PAGES/CLIVAR workshop funded by the International Geosphere Biosphere Program (IGBP) opens with the statement "The instrumental and satellite record of climate variability is too short and spatially incomplete to reveal the full range of seasonal to centennial-scale climate variability or to provide empirical examples of how the climate system responds to large changes in climate forcing..." Consequently to that say "in 50 – 100 years time I will be able to tell you whether there is global warming or whether the ozone hole is getting bigger, or whether what we are experiencing is just one of many cyclical variations" is problematic. It is dangerous to extrapolate from past incomplete and incompatible records, and care must be taken not to fall into some of these same traps in the future. Objectivity, intelligence and simple common sense will be even more essential if anything meaningful is to be obtained from this huge investment in time and money – and this not just from the scientists but also from the politicians! Science and technology will provide the data – it is up to people to provide the answers.

References

Asrar G and Dokken D J. 1993. *EOS Reference Handbook* (NASA, Washington).

Carlton A 1991. *Satellite Remote Sensing in Climatology* (Belhaven Press, London).

CEOS 1992. *The Relevance of Satellite Missions to the Study of the Global Environment* (British National Space Centre, London).

ESEF, 1996. *The Global Warming Debate* (Cambridge: European Science and Environment Forum).

Gurney R. J., Foster, J. L. and Parkinson C.I., 1993. *Atlas of Satellite Observations Related to Global Change* (Cambridge University Press).

Kramer H.J. 1996. *Observation of the Earth and its Environment – Survey of Missions and Sensors* (Springer-Verlag, Heidelberg).

Vaughan R. A. and Cracknell A. P. 1994. *Remote Sensing and Global Climate Change.* (Springer-Verlag, Heidelberg).

Vaughan R. A. *Remote Sensing – Systems and Data in Remote Sensing and Global Climate Change* (Springer-Verlag, Heidelberg).

Further reading

There are now many excellent textbooks available which describe in detail the principles and applications of all aspects of remote sensing, and even a few which discuss its use in climatology. The proceedings of a NATO-funded summer school in 1992 (Vaughan and Cracknell 1994) contains reviews on climate modelling and the inputs to it of remote sensing as well as a number of climatological applications. In 1992, the British National Space Centre published a report for the Committee on Earth Observation Satellites (CEOS) which set out the existing and proposed earth observation satellite missions for the following 15 years and described how these programmes 'would provide information crucial to the success of global environmental programmes'. The report was produced specifically for delegates attending the UNCED Conference in Rio de Janeiro. In 1993, NASA published a new edition of its reference handbook on the Earth Observing System (EOS) Programme (Asrar and Dokken 1993) which contains a useful compendium of information about present and future platforms and instruments especially designed for long-term global observations. The book by Kramers (1996) is an excellent reference book which describes almost every known satellite system and instrument as well as airborne instruments and hyperspectral scanners. This third edition describes about 129 spaceborne missions and 190 airborne sensors. The article by Vaughan (1994) contains a fuller list of references as well as a more detailed discussion of the use of remote sensing to studying global climate change.

Robin Vaughan

Robin Vaughan is a Senior Lecturer in Physics at the University of Dundee. He has been involved in remote sensing for nearly 15 years and was Director of a NATO ASI in "Remote Sensing and Global Climate Change' held in Dundee in 1992. He has published widely in the field of remote sensing. He is currently Honorary General Secretary of The Remote Sensing Society and Treasurer of the European Association of Remote Sensing Laboratories (EARSeL), Financial Director of RSS Enterprises Ltd, and a member of the Editorial Board of the International Journal of Remote Sensing and of the Board of Management of the Dundee Centre for Coastal Zones Research. Last year he was elected Fellow of The Remote Sensing Society .

Limited Predictability and the estimated Greenhouse Effect

C. Wiin-Christensen
Danish Defence Command

A. Wiin-Nielsen
University of Copenhagen, Denmark.

Summary

The weather system is chaotic or non-linear, and therefore is poorly simulated by prediction models which use linear methods. The limited predictability of non-linear systems is reviewed, using weather predictions as the first example. The simulations of the greenhouse effect using global climate models are analysed with respect to the impact of the atmospheric chaotic behaviour on the simulations. It is concluded that both the theoretical basis of the simulations and their interpretation are incorrect. Furthermore, it is pointed out that since the simulations are not based on natural climate processes, they cannot, in principle, be verified using global climate data, the first being linear, the second being chaotic.

Limited predictability

Any person interested in the weather and weather forecasts will know that predictions of sufficient accuracy can be made for a only few days in advance. As weather forecasting models improved from a physical and numerical point of view, and took advantage of increasing computing power, the practical limit of predictability increased from 24 hours to about 3½ days in 1970, since when their development has faltered.

What is the real reason that extended forecasts for the next month or the next season cannot be prepared with more than limited accuracy? After all, the calendar states sunrise and sunset for every day of the year for a given location. The coming and going of the tides are also predicted with reasonable accuracy. These predictions are, of course far from trivial, but they are quite accurate. Why not the weather?

In all these cases we are talking about predictions based on classical Newtonian physics, and Newtonian equations of motion are deterministic. This means that, for given baseline conditions, one, and only one, predicted outcome will be derived. The clue to understanding limited predictability was first discovered by Poincaré (1893) with some earlier considerations by Hill (1878). A philosophical treatment has been given by Poincaré (1912). They were concerned with the astronomical three-body problem. While the two-body problem, i.e. the hypothetical problem of finding the motion of a single planet around the Sun, was solved by Newton in a closed mathematical form, it has never been possible to solve the more general problem of the motion of two planets around the Sun in the same way. Poincaré decided that he would try to obtain a practical solution by integrating the well-known equations for the three-body problem by numerical methods. He and his assistants found that the computed tracks of the two planets were very sensitive to small changes in the baseline conditions. In other words, the computed paths of the two planets would be very different if small changes were made in the starting conditions for the two planets, relative to each other and relative to the Sun. It is this sensitivity to small changes in the starting conditions that is the real cause of limited predictability.

Poincaré's discovery was 'forgotten'. The reason is probably that those studying physics in the first decades of the present century were more concerned with the development of new theories: the theories of relativity and of the atom, while classical physics was considered uninteresting, although useful for the solutions of practical engineering problems. However, the sensitivity to small changes in the initial conditions was rediscovered by Edward N. Lorenz (1963), when he decided to investigate a small system of three equations that were a sub-system of a much larger system, which described the motion of the air between two horizontal plates. In this system, the lower plate is kept at a constant temperature while the upper plate has a constant but lower temperature. When the temperature difference between the two plates is sufficiently large, the motion of air between the plates changes character, and it becomes particularly sensitive to the starting conditions. The Lorenz-system was later named 'strange attraction'.

It was soon discovered that only non-linear equations display this sensitivity to minute changes in the initial state. Non-linear equations are those where the unknowns appear as products (say, $x \times y$), while linear equations contain only terms where an unknown is multiplied by a coefficient (say, $a \times x$). The equations for any practical atmospheric prediction model are non-linear. It is straightforward to investigate if the model suffers from limited predictability, by using available models which are integrated twice. The first integration starts from a certain initial state, the second from a slightly changed initial state. The difference between the two integrations is measured by the root-mean-square difference. In the case of the atmosphere models that we considered, the differences between the two integrations become 'unacceptable' after three or four weeks of iterations, which allows the conclusion that the theoretical limit of predictability of these models is about one month. For further reading on this, the development of chaos theory, with many examples, has been given by Lorenz (1993).

In a practical sense, when designing weather prediction models, we make a single prediction from an initial state, obtained by calculations based on the available observations. However, using standard data, supplemented by satellite observations, we are never able to describe the initial state with full accuracy. From the very beginning of the modelling process, there is therefore a difference between the **real** state and the **analysed** state. The difference between these two states will grow with time, and when the difference reaches an unacceptable level, we have reached the practical limit of predictability. Over the last quarter of a century meteorologists have improved the initial analysis and the models in such a way that the practical predictability has increased from about three-and-a-half days to about seven days. It is obvious that there is a considerable gap between the practical and the theoretical limits of predictability.

The general explanation of the limited predictability, due to both the uncertainties in the initial state and the effect of heating, will have an influence on any attempt to make climate predictions or simulations, as we shall try to describe in the next section. It is, however, necessary to explain the difference between a weather forecast and a prediction of a climatic state in some detail before we discuss the work by the IPCC.

The climate

In describing the climate, we are not interested in the changes in the weather from day to day, but rather in the general type that has dominated the weather over a longer period of time. In describing a given season we may, for example, say that in a particular year the summer was cold and wet in our region. But in order to make such a statement it is necessary to compare the averaged temperature and the precipitation for that particular summer with some standard. It is for this reason that climatologists have defined the standard summer as a time-average over many summers. To be exact, the climate at a given place is defined as the 30-year average of the various meteorological parameters, but several other averaging times are also used in practice. We cannot determine the present climate from actual observations with reasonable accuracy for more than the two climate intervals 1931-1960 and 1961-1990 (ESEF, 1990). The accuracy is better for the latter interval due to there now being more and better data, supplemented by satellite information. From ice core data and cores from the bottom of the ocean, we have some indirect information on past changes of the climate on large time scales, but it is not the purpose of the present article to deal with these matters.

We do not have a physical, quantitative theory of climate change on any of the smaller time scales. It has, for example been observed that the global mean temperature decreased from about 1935 to 1970, but a good explanation for this behaviour is still lacking. Similarly, no explanation of a quantitative nature is available for the so-called 'Little Ice Age' which dominated north-western Europe and the Atlantic region from about 1250 to about 1850. The Little Ice Age is not supposed to have been influenced by any anthropogenic effects.

Any branch of the physical sciences will go through a number of phases of development, normally called the observational, the descriptive, the predictive and the controlling phases. The weather forecast aspects of meteorology may be said to be in the third phase, while climatology has entered the descriptive phase. Normally, one should discourage any type of predictions arrived at before the natural variability has been accounted for by a well tested theory. However, the first step in this direction has been taken. Using global climate models it has been possible to simulate the major aspects of the present climate.

At this point it may be desirable to describe the major content of a climate, or, for that matter, a medium-range prediction model, since these models are very much alike. The models predict in a step-by-step procedure the time development of all the parameters describing the model. In these models it is necessary to describe in a quantitative way the physical processes in the atmosphere. Quite a number of such processes exist, but they seem to take place on the molecular scale or at least on scales that are small, compared with the scale that can be represented directly in a global model. A global climate model may be represented by a grid where the gridlength in the best cases may be 20-30 km and often more. To deal with the sub-scale problems a procedure has been invented called parameterization in which the aim is to express the net effect of a given small-scale process on the parameters representing the particular gridsquare. Such parameterization expressions are normally of a statistical nature, and it is very difficult to formulate them. Taken together, they represent an uncertainty in the specification of the energy supply to the atmosphere at any given time.

IPCC model integrations.

The IPCC integrations use various climate models in the way described above. A typical integration consists of two parts. The first part is an integration in which the anthropogenic forcing is kept constant. The second is an integration in which the anthropogenic forcing varies in time according to a certain prescription. A common example is one where the concentration of carbon dioxide in the second integration is twice as large as in the first, but another specification is one where the carbon dioxide increases to twice the original concentration in, for example, 100 years. Similar prescriptions may be included for other anthropogenic gases, such as sulphur dioxide. Many experiments containing different prescriptions are normally done. The effect of the different prescriptions for the gases will change the heating in the model (for details see IPCC, 1995 and earlier reports).

The two integrations in an experiment differ at least gradually in the heating. Since the model describes the development of a chaotic atmosphere, it will have limited predictability, as shown above. Consequently, the two integrations will differ more and more with time, partly because of the direct changes in the heating, but also because of the limited predictability. Therefore, the interpretation of the results is in principle, incorrect in ascribing the total difference to the changes in the concentrations of the anthropogenic gases. Some of the representatives of the IPCC maintain that the simulations do not behave in a chaotic way. If so, the model is not a good model for the atmosphere. It would thus appear that the conclusions drawn from the model experiments are doubtful. It has also been maintained that the above argument is incorrect due to the time-averaging of the two integrations. However, the time averages are performed after the experiments, and when the individual integrations diverge, so will their averages.

All the IPCC reports conclude that regional (and local) changes cannot be reliable. While it is true that transient, essentially free, waves will have a tendency to disappear in the averaging process, this is not true for the longer, forced waves. A large part of the amplitude of the forced waves is due to land heating and orographic, or relief effects, which keep the stationary part of the very long waves at certain preferred longitudinal locations. The changes in heating will have a marked influence on the shape and the position of the very long waves, and their longitudinal position in turn determines the places where shorter waves form, the so-called cyclone tracks. Hence the basis of the experiments is rather uncertain.

It should also be pointed out that the IPCC experiments do not make real climate change predictions. The reason is, of course, that the change in heating results only from the pre-determined prescriptions of the changes in the anthropogenic gases. The models do not contain any 'natural' effects which would predict climate changes in the absence of any anthropogenic effects. The reason is, as was pointed out above, that we do not have any theory for the natural climate changes which do occur. As a consequence, the results of the experiments cannot be compared directly with the observed variations of the climate. To put this point in more simple terms, we may say that if the global mean temperature decreases by 1 degree Celsius in the next one hundred years, one would say that a natural phenomenon had created this decrease. If, on the other hand, the temperature increased by one degree, one could not logically ascribe the increase to the greenhouse effect. It could just as easily be a natural change created by some other effect not included in the model integrations.

The major reason for the concern about the scientific foundation of any model integration of the anthropogenic type rests in the non-linearity of the basic equations and their sensitivity to even small changes in the heating. It would indeed be astonishing if climate variations were predictable without time limitations, when the validity of weather forecasts are so severely restricted by the limited predictability, since the two models are almost identical. But the non-linearity cannot be circumvented if one wants to use the full field-descriptions on the globe. On the other hand, since the statements by the IPCC are limited to the changes in the averaged temperature for the whole planet, would it be possible to limit the prediction to changes in the global mean temperature? If that were possible, one could obtain the equations for the global mean temperature by simply averaging the model equations over the whole planet and from the bottom to the top of the atmosphere. The major advantage of such a procedure would be that all the non-linear terms related to the motion in the atmosphere would vanish, and it is precisely these terms that cause the major problems.

In the further analysis of the proposal to limit the considerations to the atmospheric mean temperature, one should be aware that whenever one performs an averaging procedure there will always be a loss of information, because all reference to the variations across the Earth will disappear. This has significant consequences for prediction. In describing the physical processes influencing the overall mean temperature one is forced to deal with an 'average' Earth. It is impossible to refer to the distribution of continents and oceans. The cloud cover has to be discussed in terms of averaged amounts of clouds and averaged physical properties of clouds. Some of the interactions with positive and negative feedbacks become difficult to formulate. Nevertheless, models in which the only two dependent variables are the atmospheric mean temperature and the mean temperature of the surface of the Earth, have been formulated and are used for simulations of the anthropogenic effects.

Such models at least have the advantage that they are much simpler than the three-dimensional global climate models. The simple models have therefore at least a pedagogical advantage as an introduction to the climate change problems, and it is really for this purpose that they were invented. The other, perhaps astonishing, result is that the integrations of the simple model equations are capable of producing results that are of the same order of magnitude as the IPCC models.

Observed temperature changes

The models produce estimates of the temperature changes caused by a combination of anthropogenic effects. Since these estimates cannot be predictions of climate changes, because the climate may change due to other physical effects, it becomes very difficult to discover if the anthropogenic estimates can be found in the observations, because the observations have to be corrected due to influences of other processes (the so-called natural causes of climate change) that may change the temperatures.

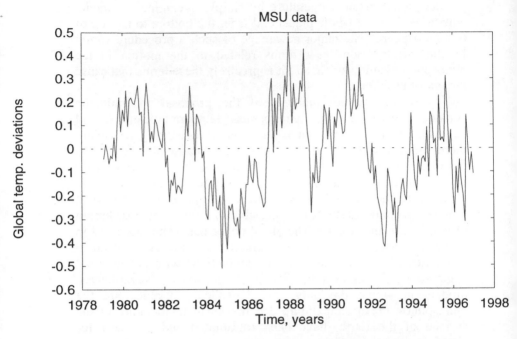

Figure 1: The observed changes of monthly mean temperatures covering the years 1979 to 1996, incl.

For the purpose of this paper it will suffice to reproduce one of the best records of lower tropospheric temperatures. These data, obtained from a microwave sounder, will be named the MSU data. They cover the years 1979-1996 inclusive. Figure 1 shows the monthly deviations from the average for the decade 1982-1991, measured in degrees Kelvin. We notice some, occasionally large, deviations from one month to the next. In addition, we see a change of sign in the deviations on a larger time scale. The overall average change of the global data is -0.0095 degrees. This slight decrease is not significantly different from zero, as can be seen by conducting one of the usual statistical tests. Based on these data it is thus not possible to determine a significant trend in the lower troposphere global mean temperatures. The changes on a larger time scale are seen more clearly in Figure 2 containing the 12 month running mean of the data in Figure 1. The record of observations from other sources, such as tropospheric temperatures from radiosonde data show, no significant trend either.

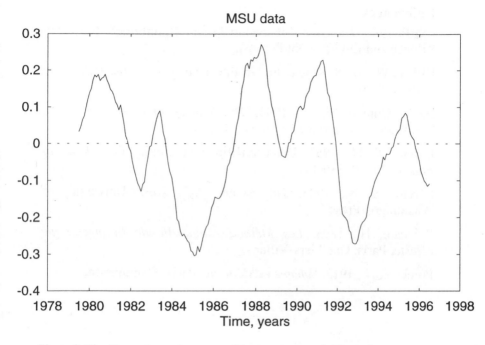

Figure 2: The 12 month running mean of the temperatures in Figure 1

Concluding remarks

The present review of the possibilities of modelling and observing anthropogenic temperature changes indicates that one of the best actions for the future is to monitor atmospheric temperature changes. In addition, it would make sense to support researchers who promise to be able to find the major reasons for climatic changes on various time scales. If successful, one could obtain some of the elements of a basic quantitative theory for the climate and its changes.

References

ESEF, 1996. *The Global Warming Debate* (Cambridge: European Science and Environment Forum).

Hill, G.W., 1878. Researches in the lunar theory. *Amer. Jour. of Math.* I, 5-26.

IPCC: Climate Change 1995, *The Science of Climate Change*, Cambridge: Cambridge University Press.

Lorenz, E. N., 1963. Deterministic nonperiodic flow. *Jour. of Atmos. Sci.* 20, 130-141.

Lorenz, E. N., 1993. *The Essence of Chaos*. University of Washington Press.

Poincaré, H., 1893. *Les Méthodes nouvelle de la mécanique céleste*. Paris: Gauthiers-Villar.

Poincaré, H., 1912. *Science et Méthode*. Paris: Flammarion.

Charlotte Wiin-Christensen

Charlotte Wiin-Christensen, was educated in U.S.A. and UK and earned a Bachelor's degree from the University of Reading in 1977, and a Master's degree in Atmospheric Sciences, University of Copenhagen, 1985. Employed by Denmark's Meteorological Institute, 1977-1994, Staff Meteorologist at the Danish Defence Command from 1994. She is the author of a popular book entitled *Climate Problems* (Teknisk Forlag, Denmark) and several scientific papers on the problem of blocking in the atmosphere.

Aksel Wiin-Nielsen

Aksel Wiin-Nielsen is Professor Emeritus at the University of Copenhagen. Former positions include: Professor and Chairman, Department of Atmospheric and Oceanic Sciences, University of Michigan; Director of the European Centre for Medium-Range Forecasts, Reading, Berks, U.K.; and Secretary General, the World Meteorological Organization.

Bias in measured data

A. H. Gordon
School of Earth Sciences
Flinders University
Adelaide
South Australia

Summary

In the several years preceding the formulation of the IPCC, normally responsible scientists issued ill-considered statements about global warming. It was hoped that the IPCC would bring a more objective scientific approach to the issue. To some extent this was true in the early stages, but as the years went by, human bias in the official utterances by IPCC scientists or administrators became more and more evident. Specific examples were press releases after the Maastricht meeting on radiative forcing, the rush to announce that 1995 was the warmest year on record even before the year finished and, more recently, the extreme sensitivity of IPCC scientists to criticisms of the bottom line statement that "the balance of evidence suggests a detectable human influence on climate", a conclusion many scientists find unproved. Further criticisms of the IPCC scientific method include its selective use of evidence, and its overstatement of consensus on global warming among 2500 scientists, given that it is doubtful that there is a tenth that number of atmospheric scientists in the world who are appropriately qualified to give an informed opinion.

Here, the Second Assessment Report Chapter 3 on the observational record is examined. Points of bias, some of a minor nature, are pinpointed. The most important fact to bring out is that the troposphere as a whole has not warmed at all during the last 18 years. A tentative suggestion is made that the observed warming at the surface is a boundary layer phenomenon that is not caused by the radiative heating of carbon dioxide. It may instead be due to the trapping of heat in the boundary layer caused by a shift in other terms of the planet's heat budget.

Ms. Elizabeth Dowdeswell, Executive Director of the United Nations Environment Program (UNEP), in her opening address to the 12th session of the IPCC in Mexico City in September 1996 remarked: "The United States Under-Secretary of State for Global Affairs spoke for many of us when he castigated those few who, in the face of the most rigorously reviewed international assessment of all time, challenged the IPCC conclusions".

What an extraordinary thing to say to a meeting presumably called to discuss scientific matters. Can we no longer challenge orthodoxies? The entire ethos of scientific thinking is continually to challenge theories and ideas, while at the same time formulating new ones. Only in this way can science truly advance.

It is a sad sign of modern times that statements of the kind made at the IPCC meeting should be allowed to pass by without comment by the assembled body.

This article presents an assessment of Chapter 3 of the IPCC Second Assessment Report (SAR), which presents and discusses the observational records of temperature, precipitation, water vapour content, and other meteorological derivatives. This approach is marked by emphasising evidence of warming where it has been observed to occur, while tending to discount cooling by omission rather than argument. There is no in-depth exposition of stochastic mechanisms which could, in part, be responsible for some of the observed results.

Chapter 3 could be regarded as the most important chapter in the entire SAR volume. It deals with the facts of observed results in so far as they describe the climate. Other chapters deal with the theory of climate, the physical processes which determine climate, the chemistry of the atmosphere, the construction of models and their output, the validation of different models, the detection of a human-induced climate signal, and so forth. Chapter 3 should be the backbone of the SAR. The chapters on models can be over-emphasized. Models can be and are tuned and adjusted to reproduce the real world as it has happened. This does not mean that they can predict or reproduce what will happen in the future. Non-linearity, random noise and sensitive dependence leading to bifurcations and chaos are some of the reasons why it is difficult for models to predict the future in contrast to reproducing the past. Although the modelling community recognises these problems and has devised new ways such as making an ensemble of forecasts, each of which starts with a slightly different initial condition, the problem has not yet been solved. It may never be.

An example of the fallibility of models is that early results described in the IPCC First Assessment Report appeared to exaggerate the global warming trends. Later it was theorised that sulphate aerosols contained in industrial emissions produced a cooling effect. This effect was subsequently included in models, so producing a smaller warming trend in the computed simulation than had previously been the case. This kind of procedure can, of course, be continued indefinitely.

Chapter 3 should therefore be oriented towards challenging the implied conclusions of other chapters rather than subtly trying to support them. But the plan adopted can well be seen to provoke the often made evaluation "the most rigorously reviewed (and prepared) international assessment of all time"

We find that this chapter has: six lead authors, seven key contributors, 95 contributors, and 380 references.

Michaels (1996b) pointed out that Chapter 3, along with the other chapters of IPCC SAR contains a number of improper citations. These include technical reports, book chapters, conference proceedings, previous IPCC reports, and papers that have been submitted or in process of publication, and so not available for general reference. But perhaps the greatest fault is one of default, one of selectivity, one of ignoring other published work which perhaps does not fit into the desired pattern, one of failing to adequately discuss possible interpretations of the information presented, other than the subtly implied one of greenhouse gas induced warming.

We will look at one or two of the more striking examples of problems which arise in this chapter.

Land surface temperatures

On page 141 of SAR, it is stated that "[t]he 19th century Australian temperatures may be biased warm relative to modern recordings because of different methods of exposure". This would suggest that warming trends in Australian temperatures could be greater than reported. The latter conclusion is based on a study made by a group of students at Australia's Swinburne Institute of Technology. The study containing the results was an internal unrefereed report. A similar implication is subsequently made that this bias may extend to all Northern hemisphere summer temperatures, but this study is better documented (Parker 1994). The Swinburne report has since been effectively discounted (Hughes 1997). It is surprising that an unverified statement of this kind should have passed the hundreds of contributors and reviewers who constitute the review process.

No mention is made of the seasonal cycle of Northern Hemisphere summer land temperature trends. The trend in July is almost negligible, while in the winter months it is quite pronounced. (Figure 1). Some further comment about this remarkable annual cycle, additional to the single sentence in 3.3.4, p.157 which quite reasonably suggests that changes in snow cover might be responsible for the increased Northern Hemisphere land trends in spring, would have been most useful.

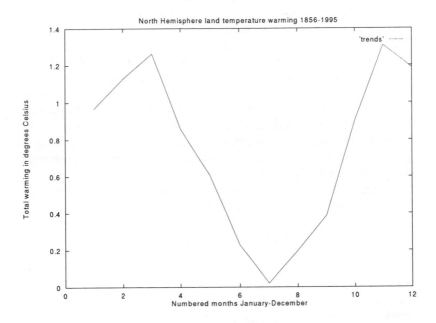

Figure 1: Northern Hemisphere summer land temperature warming 1856-1995

The MSU satellite record

In 1990 a paper was published by Spencer and Christy giving the results of a study of the first ten years of the record of the MSU satellite's recorded observations of temperature anomalies in the troposphere. The calculations showed no appreciable trend. Ever since then, that is, for the past six years, the IPCC have had difficulty in reconciling these results with those exhibited by surface records. Although it is clearly stated in section 3.3.3, p.147 that the global MSU temperature trend from January 1979 through May 1995 was -0.06°C/decade, and that for the radiosonde data for the same period it was -0.07°C/decade, these facts cannot be accepted by the lead authors without qualification. Thus, they introduce the concept that transient effects due to volcanoes and ENSO (El Niño Southern Oscillation) are really responsible for the difference between the surface and upper air records for this overlapping period. After making the appropriate empirical adjustments for volcanoes and ENSO they say that positive trends of about 0. 10°C/decade emerge.

Yet, it is then stated that if one considers the rather longer period for which radiosonde data are available (1958-1995), there is no real need to make any adjustments since the trend is about 0.10°C/decade without making the adjustments. The authors finally conclude that there is no need to make adjustments for longer periods because "the results reflect the result that longer term trends are less likely to be biased by transient volcanic and ENSO influences". Actually, the statement attributed to Jones (1995) that the complete radiosonde record shows a trend of about 0.10°C/decade is incorrect. Michaels (1996b) has shown that there is no significant trend during this period.

This argument may appear to be of dubious validity. Volcanoes and ENSO are and always have been an inherent part of our planet's behaviour. The truth cannot be hidden by tampering with results which appear to differ from the consensus view.

Figure 3.7, p.148 purports to show plots of surface, radiosonde and MSU on one diagram. The diagram is poorly drawn and is a visual illusion to suggest there is little difference between the three sets of observations. But if the diagram had been more clearly drawn and the scale enlarged, the differences between the surface and MSU, and the surface and the radiosonde would become obvious, and present a serious and unexplained problem.

Figure 2 (a, b) in this article gives a much better picture of the trends of the surface and satellite data for the period January 1979 – June 1996 for the two hemispheres. Twelve-month running averages have been used which gives a much less noisy plot than a plot of the individual months. There are big differences between the satellite and surface land marine mix records. First, the satellite traces are almost continuously less than the surface traces in both hemispheres. Second, the trends are different. In the Northern Hemisphere the total temperature change for the period computed by linear regression is 0.3°C. The satellite trend is -0.01°C, insignificantly different from zero. In the Southern Hemisphere the land trace has a trend of 0.1°C whereas the satellite trace is -0.2 °C, a substantial fall. The difference between the trends of the surface and satellite observations is the same for both hemispheres at 0.3°C, a most interesting result.

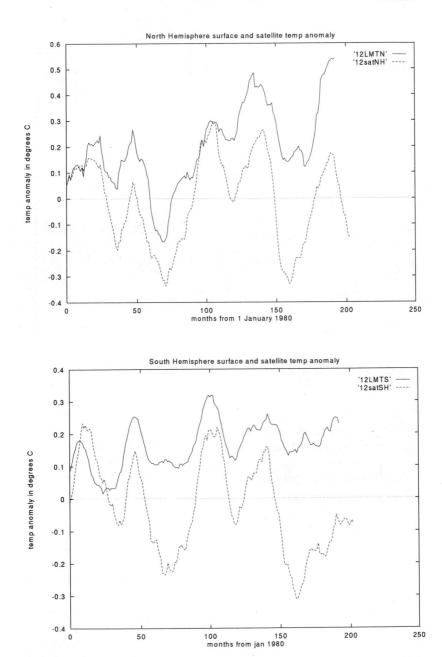

Figures 2a,b: North and South Hemisphere surface and satellite temperature anomaly.

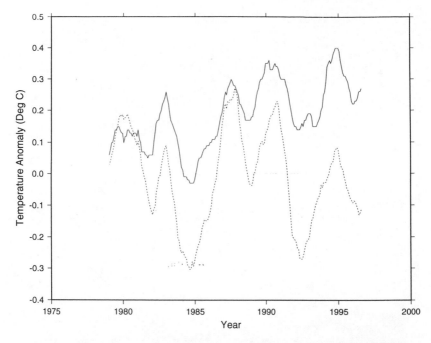

Figure 3. 12-month running average temperature anomalies for the global land marine temperature (solid line) and the global satellite temperature (dashed line).

Figure 3 shows the 12-month running averages of the mean monthly global temperature anomalies for the surface and satellite records for the period January 1979-June 1997. The divergence of the trends of the surface and satellite records is most striking; it is a fact that must be explained before firm conclusions can be drawn about global warming.

Other minor points of contention

In the case of the California coast, it is stated that "off California (a region of surface warming), sub surface temperatures have increased uniformly by 0.8°C in the upper 100 metres in the past 42 years, and have been significant" (SAR 3.2.4, p.149). But anyone who has lived in California knows that for 6 months of the year the coastal climate is determined by upwelling producing a cold current from Eureka to Baja California. This upwelling is driven by the Pacific summer anticyclone. Any change in the strength of the oceanic high pressure system will be directly coupled with upwelling, with ocean surface temperatures, and with the entire coastal climate. Yet this section seems to imply that the observed warming is another CO_2-induced greenhouse signal.

The chapter is, in many places, subtly suggestive that the climate has warmed more rapidly during recent years than might be expected from natural variability. For example, on p.179 we find that "in at least some regions 20th century temperatures have been warmer than any other century for some thousands of years." It is difficult to see how such a conclusion is reached from the figures presented. Results from ice cores represent an extremely limited area of the earth's surface, and there are doubts about the reliability of applying these proxy methods to the real atmosphere. And the reconstruction of past climates shows huge sudden changes, as much at $7°C$ in a few decades (p.178).

In the final section, it is stated "the observed warming cannot be attributed to urbanization since it is also found in ocean temperatures"(3.7). This is not true. Land and ocean temperatures are coupled and adjust to one another in a few months. The land would not get warmer indefinitely while the sea stayed the same. What is not said here is that the troposphere has not warmed at all since 1979. It is the boundary layer which has warmed.

Perhaps urbanization is not the right term to use to explain trends in the boundary layer. Such observed warming trends could have been caused (if physical, as opposed to stochastic cause there must be) by changes in the upward heat flux from the land surface due to artificial changes in the earth's land surface, overgrazing of pasture land, deforestation, urban sprawl and the sheer magnitude of an ever increasing heat producing population. It is estimated (SAR) that about 44% of the long wave radiation absorbed by and emitted to space by the atmosphere is in the form of thermals and evapotranspiration. Much of the heat embodied in the latter two forms may be trapped in the boundary layer which extends from the surface to about 700 metres above the surface of the ground. This amounts to some 72 watts/sq.m. So a 3% increase in this amount is of the same order of magnitude as the greenhouse gas forcing, and importantly, it acts in the places where thermometer screens are positioned.

The scenario described above does bring its own set of problems. If the boundary layer warming exceeds some critical amount it will create unstable lapse rates which will set off convective instabilities, which in turn will warm the troposphere (and cool the boundary layer). But this does not appear to have happened yet.

Chapter 3 is very important as it deals with real data and the real world. Models can be tuned to reproduce and simulate greenhouse warming and aerosol cooling as shown by Santer et al. (1996), but in the end it is the real world which will yield the answer. The theoretical basis of the enhanced greenhouse effect is that the radiative properties of greenhouse gases cause warming. The test of the issue is 'has the troposphere warmed, and if so is it due to anthropogenic or natural causes?' In this respect all we know is that the boundary layer as measured by thermometers in screens a metre or so above the ground surface has warmed, and is apparently continuing to do so. The troposphere does not seem to have warmed at all during the last 17 years, and probably only inappreciably, if at all, for the past 38 years during which radiosonde measurements have been made (Michaels, 1996a).

The all-encompassing issue which has been seized upon by governments and non-governmental organisations of many colours is covered by the umbrella expression 'climate change'. But the scientific issue is global warming. That must first be determined before the broader concept of 'climate change' is tackled. However, the general public, as well as many who are at the fringe of the science, confuse the issue by failing to understand the difference. So any unusual event is treated as evidence of climate change, even if there is no obvious connection. Unusual snowfalls, frosts and exceptional winter cold spells are seized upon with as much fervour as are unusual summer hot spells as proof of climate change. It is as if the proponents of climate change have lost the plot altogether and have forgotten or misunderstood the physics upon which the entire concept rests.

Little knowledge of the existence of anthropogenic global warming can be gleaned from isolated pieces of information such as Chapter 3 revels in. A piece of bleached coral in the Barrier Reef off the Queensland coast, a growth of green on some coastal shore of Antarctica, an incident of some tropical illness, or of food poisoning in a temperate zone country are, neither individually nor collectively, evidence of climate change.

Although Chapter 3 is concerned with the observational record rather than with physical processes and explanations, it would not have been inappropriate to include some discussion on the stochastic nature of climate variability, on the possible forcing of the observations by random noise, without intruding into the domains of modellers and physicists. A widening of the chapter's terms of reference would have given readers of all persuasions a less biased picture of the enormous issues at stake.

References

Jones, P., *Geophys.Res.Lett.*,21,1149-52.

Hughes, W., *Int. Jour. Clim.*,17,1-3,1997.

IPCC, Second Assessment Report, Cambridge University Press, 1996.

Michaels, P., The Global Warming Debate, ESEF, 1996a.

Michaels, P., *Nature*, 384,522-23,1996b.

Parker, D. E., *Int.Jour,Clim.*,14,1-3.

Santer et al, B., *Nature* 382, 39-46, 1996.

Spencer, R.G. and J. Christy, *Science*, 247,1558-1562, 1990.

Adrian Gordon

Dr A. H. Gordon obtained his BSc in physics in 1935, and his M.Sc. in meteorology in 1936, both from Cal Tech. He served with the UK Meteorological Office from 1936 to 1963, and then with the UNDP in Iran and the Philippines, where he was Visiting Professor of Meteorology at the Universities of Tehran and Manila. He was associate professor of geosciences at the University of Hawaii from 1965 to 1967.

He obtained his PhD in meteorology from Flinders University, South Australia, in 1986, after his retirement. Since 1987 he has undertaken research into global warming and related topics and has published numerous papers in refereed journals on this and other subjects in meteorology and climatology. He is the author of a textbook on elementary dynamic meteorology.

Smudged Fingerprint: The Elusive Search for a Human Impact on the Climate System

Gerd-Rainer Weber
Essen
Germany

Introduction – The road to Madrid and Rome

The bombshell struck on 20 February 1995. During a press conference at the German ministry of Science and Technology, German minister Ruttgers and the head of the German Climate Modelling Centre in Hamburg, Hasselmann, declared that they – with 95% confidence – could demonstrate a human impact on the climate system in recent decades. Hasselmann's group had analysed climate trends observed in recent decades and concluded that the magnitude of those trends was larger than could be ascribed to either modelled or observed natural climate variability (Hegerl et al., 1994).

Thus the debate started. That the announcement came from Hasselmann was appropriate, since he had been involved in the development of statistical techniques called 'fingerprint techniques' for the detection and attribution of man-made climate change for some time. In fact, he laid some of the theoretical groundwork as early as the 1970s. There was relatively slow progress in the 1980s with some work being done – in addition to Hasselmann – by Tim Barnett of SIO (Scripps Institution of Oceanography, La Jolla, California).

From the standpoint of climate science, detection and attribution of any human impact on the climate system is one of the critical issues. The debate over climate change, particularly when it came to demanding and actually implementing political measures to combat climate change, had always foundered in the past because any prediction of future climate change was just that: a prediction which one might believe or not believe. Greenhouse gas concentrations in the atmosphere have already gone up to the halfway point of a CO_2 doubling (the usual benchmark frequently used in climate model calculations), therefore one should already see close to half of the warming (adjusted for the slowing effect of the oceans). The actual extent of the observed warming, being considerably less than that, was a major nuisance to those calling for immediate and drastic political action to combat global change. The line officially taken by the IPCC in 1990, but also in 1992, was that the observed warming 'was broadly compatible' with climate model predictions. It was modified by natural factors, which may exert a temporary cooling, but also a warming effect. All this was about to change in 1995. If one could actually not only detect a warming, but attribute it to the action of man-made emissions, the political leverage for demanding countermeasures would be increased.

The next piece after Hasselmann's February coup fell into place at the first Conference of the Parties to the UNFCCC (known as COP1) in Berlin, which took place in March-April 1995. Just before COP1, the UK Meteorological Office's Hadley Centre published a glossy brochure in which they demonstrated the joint modelled impact of greenhouse gas and sulphur emissions on the climate system. The point was that greenhouse gases warm the climate, but sulphur, which is also emitted by fossil fuel burning, cools it. While greenhouse gases have a long atmospheric lifetime of several years, meaning they're being mixed well in the atmosphere after about a year, sulphur only resides a short time in the atmosphere, typically a few days, meaning any cooling effects will be short lived and occur relatively close to the emission region only. In a model that considers both greenhouse gases and sulphur, one will see a regional signature in the combined effect assuming the magnitude of cooling and warming effect is large enough to show up. The regional differentiation of modelled warming is part two of the fingerprint.

Across the globe, the cooling effect is calculated to be about half as large as the warming by greenhouse gases. Therefore, sulphates effectively cancel out half the warming by greenhouse gases alone when one considers the past 100 years. The obvious benefit of this is that one could now explain why the observed warming was a lot less than the modelled warming (Mitchell et al., 1995). In fact, this piece, published in *Nature*, marks the first time leading contributors to the IPCC process publicly acknowledged that the modelled climate warming was too large, a claim long made by critics of, and dismissed by, the IPCC .

An additional study central to the attribution claim was published in late 1994 (Karoly et al., 1994). It concerned the vertical temperature structure of the atmosphere in recent decades in response to an increase of greenhouse gases alone. The conclusion was that the observed changes in the vertical temperature structure of the atmosphere observed between 1963 and 1987 could not be explained by natural factors alone.

Ben Santer researched in areas charted by the work of Hasselmann and Barnett. He and his co-workers developed a specific statistical technique that incorporated the spatial structure of climate parameters. By the end of 1995, Santer, who was also lead author of Chapter 8 of the IPCC Second Assessment Report (SAR) on detection and attribution, published two major pieces on the detection and attribution issue in 1995.

The first, published in December 1995 (Santer et al., 1995a) defined a statistical representation of the spatial temperature distribution at the earth's surface over the last 90 years and concluded that there is a correlation growing in time between observed and modelled patterns when including the regionalised cooling effect of sulphates. There was no such increasing correlation when considering greenhouse gases alone.

The second was a study which analysed the vertical temperature distribution of the atmosphere in response to not only the modelled impact of a greenhouse gas increase, as the Karoly et al. (1994) study had done, but also the response to the modelled impact of sulphate emissions and observed stratospheric ozone decrease (Santer et al., 1995b). Importantly, this study, like the one by Hegerl et al. (1994), had not been published in a peer-reviewed journal when the IPCC plenary body met in November and December 1995.

Nonetheless, it, along with the other work described here, forms the basis for the conclusions drawn at the end of the final published version of Chapter 8 of the SAR. Interestingly, most of the work central to the attribution claim was written by some of the lead authors of Chapter 8, who were then, in essence, reviewing their own work and deriving conclusions from it.

Attentive readers of *Science* and *Nature* saw the groundwork for the debate being laid in 1995. There was a steady flow of articles by the main IPCC authors and commentators indicating that human impact on the climate system was soon to be proved (e.g. Kerr, 1995a, 1995b, 1995c; Mahsood, 1995, *Nature* News, 1995). As we now know, those pieces were referring exactly to the work described above.

Strangely, at the same time, there was also a relatively steady flow of articles in other journals (see references in subsequent paragraphs) indicating that natural factors played a decisive role in the climate fluctuations observed in recent decades – leaving the observant reader somewhat at a loss.

With all that in mind, the second bombshell struck in late 1995 when the IPCC plenary body declared, in the policy maker's summary (SPM), that "the balance of evidence suggests a discernible human influence on global climate". This statement came as something of a surprise because, from the documents and scientific publications widely known at that time, including the October 1995 draft version of the now infamous Chapter 8 of the SAR, it certainly was not readily apparent.

The big question was: What do they know that we do not know? Confusion lasted almost six months until the official publication of the SAR in May 1996. The answer was to be found at the end of Chapter 8.

While the scientific content of Chapter 8 was left completely untouched from the October 1995 draft version, the conclusion now drawn from the same facts in the draft version of the chapter was entirely different. The conclusions set forth in the SPM were simply retrofitted into Chapter 8. If the body of statistical evidence shown in Chapter 8 had supported this conclusion, this would have been in order. It is not clear how the same statistical evidence can support both the conclusion in the draft that "...we don't know when attribution will be possible..." and the statement that "there is a discernible human influence (now)" in the final version.

The case for a human impact in Chapter 8 of the SAR

The key to understanding the claim of a human impact on the climate system apparently lies in the scientific work referred to in Chapter 8. While some of this work was not available to a wider scientific audience late in 1995, most of it now is. The claim revolves around four main issues:

1. Improved global temperature trend model simulations when considering the impact of both greenhouse gases and sulphates on surface air temperature between 1860 and 1990 (Mitchell et al., 1995).

2. Increasing regional pattern correlations in time when considering the influence of both greenhouse gases and sulphates on surface air temperature during the last 90 years (Santer et al., 1995a).

3. Improved pattern correlation when considering the impact of greenhouse gases, sulphates and stratospheric ozone depletion on the vertical structure of the atmosphere (Karoly et al., 1994; Santer et al., 1995b; Santer et al., 1996).

4. The claim that a sharp global temperature increase between the 1970s and the 1990s is larger than can be explained by natural variability alone (Hegerl et al., 1994; 1996).

A common thread running through every aspect of this work is the contention – or assumption – that the observed patterns cannot be explained by natural variability alone, an important point to which we will return.

The role of sulphates in climate models and observations

Let us consider first of all the work of Santer et al. (1995a) and Mitchell et al. (1995) which deals with the combined impact of sulphur and greenhouse gas emissions on surface air temperature.

Both groups of authors conducted experiments in which the combined impact of the concomitant emission of sulphur and CO_2 was modelled. While CO_2 is thought to have a warming influence, sulphur has a cooling effect. Important to note in this context is the fact that CO_2 has a much longer atmospheric residence time than SO_2 (measured in decades rather than days) and is nearly evenly distributed throughout the atmosphere, whereas sulphur and its chemical derivatives have a distinct regional distribution.[1] Therefore, the ensuing modelled cooling effect of sulphur also has a characteristic and distinct regional distribution. One should bear in mind though that there is a difference between the regional distribution of sulphur emissions, the regional distribution of ensuing forcing and the region of response when looking for sulphur effects.

It should further be borne in mind that in the case of Mitchell et al. (1995) the modelling approach used is so-called transient experiments, in which the greenhouse gas increase in the atmosphere is quasi-realistically modelled through the decades of the modelling experiments. The same goes for sulphur emissions, where the geographic distribution is very important, and relatively

---

[1] See the article by Segalstad in this volume.

well known (Dignon and Hameed, 1989; Geschwandtner et al., 1986). The distribution in time, which would also be important here, is often modelled on the basis of 1980 emissions, which were then linearly interpolated between the beginning and the end of the experiment (Mitchell et al., 1995) so that the relative geographic distribution did not change in time, which is a simplifying assumption. It is well known that sulphur emissions originating in western Europe and in North America nearly peaked in the 1930s to 1950s and have increased by a small amount only in the 1960s (Dignon and Hameed, 1989) and have decreased ever since (OECD, 1995). Worldwide emissions increased drastically after 1950 due to a large increase of fossil fuel use in the former Soviet Union and in Asia (Dignon and Hameed, 1989). Therefore, when looking for a time-dependant regional 'cooling fingerprint', one would expect to see one in the first half of the twentieth century over and downwind of North America and western Europe and in the second half of the twentieth century over and downwind of central and east Asia.

The modelled results of sulphur effects generally show maximum negative forcing over the eastern US, south-eastern Europe and eastern Asia. Maximum forcing is generally between -6 and -10 Wm^{-2}, eclipsing modelled greenhouse gas-related forcing over the areas in question (by and large around 2.5 Wm^{-2} at present), by a substantial margin. Consequently, the net effect is a large negative forcing over those areas, which ultimately leads to a modelled cooling. In a global average the cooling effect presumably is around -1 Wm^{-2}, thereby 'cancelling out' almost 50% of the greenhouse gas related warming. When calculating an average global temperature trend over the last 100 to 130 years, the modelled warming becomes much smaller when sulphate is included. It is then in much better agreement with the observed temperature trend (Mitchell et al., 1995). Thus, the large difference between the observed and the modelled global trend when sulphate is not included may be explained by the cooling action of sulphates. Mitchell et al. (1995) did not specifically analyse regional patterns in a 'fingerprint' approach as Santer et al. (1995a) did, but the results on calculated temperature change published by the Hadley Centre (1995) does allow some investigation of regional temperature change patterns (see Fig 1).

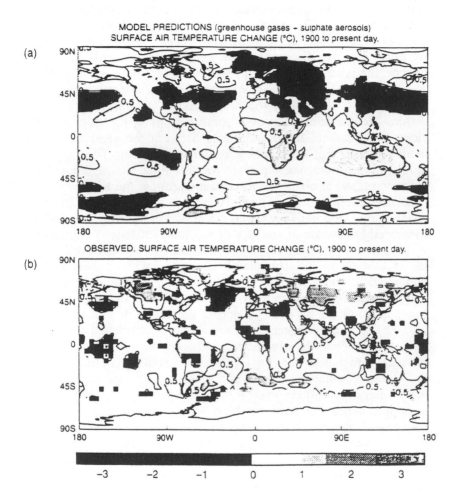

Figure 1: Surface air temperature change (°C) between 1900 (mean over the period 1880-1920) and present day (mean from 1970-1990).

Noticeable in the model are areas of warming at high latitudes and over the continental interiors, particularly over the southern hemisphere. Areas of cooling are prominent over the eastern US and the western Atlantic, over eastern Europe, central Asia, south east Asia and the western Pacific, as would be expected from the predominance of the sulphate cooling effect over those areas. The Hadley Centre (1995) also conveniently provides the observed temperature trends. Here, the largest warming can be discerned over central Asia, south western Europe, the north-western North American continent and over the southern mid latitude oceans. Areas of cooling are apparent over the central North Pacific, the north-western North Atlantic, the eastern Mediterranean and over some regions in the tropics. On closer examination, the dissimilarity between the areas of peak modelled warming and cooling becomes apparent: The area of modelled maximum cooling over western Asia almost coincides with the region of observed maximum warming, the large area of modelled cooling over eastern Asia is largely missing in the observations, the modelled maximum warming over Australia (presumably because of the lack of sulphate emissions) coincides with an area of cooling and the maximum cooling observed near the southern tip of Greenland coincides with a secondary maximum of modelled warming. Similarity, on the other hand, may be claimed over northern Siberia, Alaska and the eastern Mediterranean. In an average across the northern mid-latitudes (30–60°N), there appears to be a slight modelled cooling (particularly over the continents), whereas in the observations there appears to be a warming (particularly over the continents). In the southern hemisphere, there is a preponderance of warming in model and observations, even though the pattern correspondence does not appear to be very high (modelled warming mostly continental, observed warming mostly oceanic).

The observed temperature change over the continents of the southern and northern hemisphere between 1860 and the present is shown in Figure 2a (from Jones et al., 1986a, b and updates). There is no discernible difference in trend. It is further important to note that there is no consistent difference in trend no matter which time period one considers. For example, between 1940 and 1975, the southern hemisphere did warm up more than the northern hemisphere, but between 1955 and 1993 it did not (Fig. 2b).

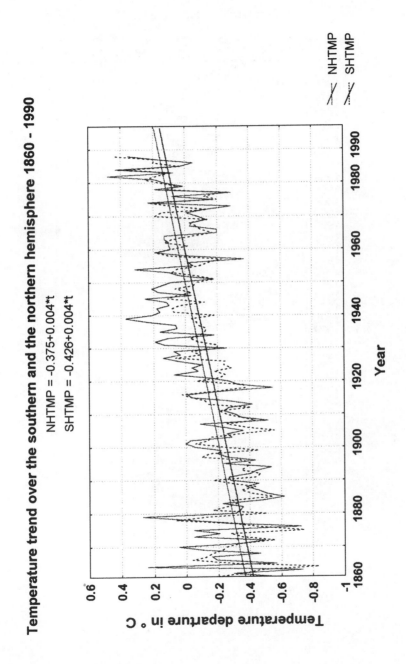

Figure 2a: Temperature trend over the southern and northern hemisphere 1860-1990

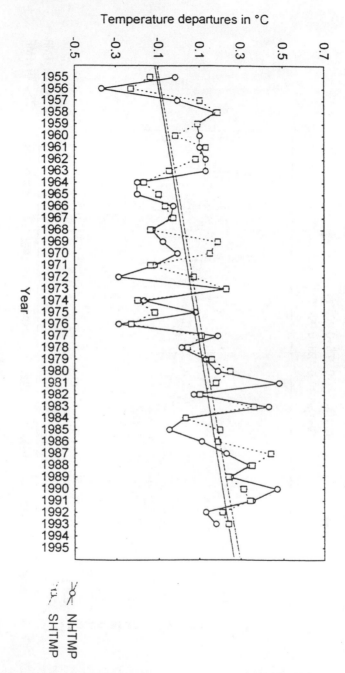

Figure 2b: Temperature trend in the Northern and Southern Hemisphere between 1955-1993

The sulphate hypothesis is not supported if differential warming of the southern hemisphere is limited to a short, specific time frame only, and if such a warming is not apparent in all other time frames.

Therefore, despite the claim that the inclusion of sulphur has led to a more realistic modelling of the spatial warming patterns, this cannot be demonstrated convincingly. Even the most basic effect – namely the interhemispheric difference – is not apparent in the observations; not to speak of the lack of congruence in the more detailed patterns described above.

Nonetheless, the Hadley Centre (1995) and Mitchell et al. (1995) claim (see their respective Figures) that in a global average, there is a better correspondence when sulphur is included.

Considering the foregoing, it appears as if the better global correspondence (reduced warming in the global average) was achieved by 'overcooling' the northern hemisphere (cf. modelled cooling maxima in northern mid-latitudes vs. observed warming maximum), which more than cancelled out 'overwarming' over the southern continents. Therefore, the increased congruence between the modelled and observed global temperature trend has been achieved by assuming excessively large sulphate cooling. Put simply: excessive (modelled) greenhouse warming has been cancelled by excessive (modelled) sulphur cooling. Thus the better correspondence is not a result of a model improvement, but because two wrongs happened to cancel each other out. It is debatable whether this constitutes an advance in knowledge.

The second important piece of work on the combined impact of greenhouse gases and sulphur on surface air temperature is the one by Santer et al. (1995a). Much of what has been said above regarding regional and temporal sulphate emission patterns applies here as well. In contrast to the Hadley Centre and Mitchell et al. (1995), Santer et al. (1995) extensively analysed spatial and temporal pattern congruence between modelled and observed surface air temperature trends. Their period of analysis is 1910–1993. The temperature change pattern modelled on the basis of present day CO_2 concentration and sulphur emissions is compared successively through that time to the observed temperature pattern. A statistic is calculated along that time axis which measures the degree of pattern congruence between modelled and observed change. Three model experiments are conducted: First, one in which CO_2 alone was increased to present day levels; another, in which only sulphur emissions were prescribed given present day emission pattern and source strengths used by Taylor and Penner (1994); and finally a third, in which both CO_2 and sulphur emissions were used at present day levels. The result of the first experiment (CO_2 alone) was that there is no significant pattern congruence in recent decades, and it does not increase in time. The result of the second experiment (sulphates only) is that there is initially, between 1910 and 1920, a fair amount of pattern congruence, decreasing pattern congruence in the later decades (1920–1950), but a large jump of pattern congruence between 1950 and 1970 in summer and autumn and a slight decline since then. Finally, in the combined experiment (CO_2 and sulphur) there is also an initial fair amount of pattern congruence in 1910–1920, a subsequent decrease and a large jump in pattern congruence between 1950 and 1970 in summer and autumn and no significant change since then. The authors further show that the trends in pattern congruence become more significant, and thereby seemingly more credible, the further back in time one goes, which says nothing more than that between 1970 and 1990, there was no significant further increase of pattern congruence.

Nevertheless, the biggest jump occurred in 1950–1970 both in the sulphate-only and in the combined greenhouse gases and sulphate experiment. It seems then as if the increase in pattern congruence can primarily be attributed to the sulphate cooling effect since the CO_2-only experiment did not contribute much to increasing pattern congruence during that time; in fact this decreased between 1940 and 1970 (see Santer et al. 1995a; their Figure 6).

The period 1950–1970 was a period of global cooling (see e.g. Jones et al., 1886,a,b) and of a large world-wide increase of sulphur emissions. Obviously, some of the areas of modelled cooling must have coincided with some of the areas of observed cooling during that time. Those areas should primarily be those where the largest response to sulphur emissions occurred (see their Fig. 2), similar to the ones shown in the Hadley Centre (1995) report.

A few additional points should now be considered. As demonstrated above, the largest sulphur emission increase over North America and western Europe occurred not between 1950 and 1970 but between 1900 and ca. 1940 (see Fig. 3). Yet this time period coincides with large warming over the continents and the higher latitudes of the northern hemisphere (e.g. Jones et al., 1986a). Not surprisingly, the pattern congruence in the sulphate-only experiment of Santer et al. (1995; their fig. 7; see also Fig. 1d in Taylor and Penner, 1994) decreases, because the observed temperature increases where it should decrease under the sulphate hypothesis.

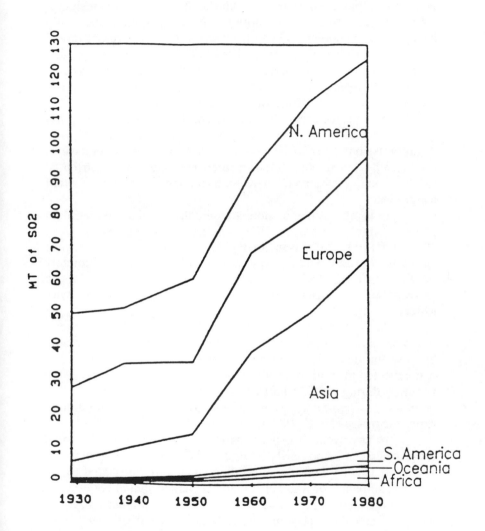

Figure 3: Regional SO_2-emissions between 1930 and 1980 (in mio t SO_2)

The pattern congruence, then, improves between 1950 and 1970, because temperature actually decreases over the same sulphate affected areas where it increased a few decades previously, even though there is now only a relatively small increase in sulphur emissions over North America and western

Europe. Pattern congruence now increases because cooling occurs in those regions where it should according to the sulphate model.

Clearly, the real atmosphere responded in two different ways to sulphate emissions: in the first part of this century, warming, in the second half, cooling! Therefore, if sulphates really have the strong cooling effect attributed to them in present model calculations, this cooling effect should already have been present in the first half of the century. Instead, the atmosphere reacted with the strongest warming seen in recent centuries over exactly the same areas where strongest cooling is modelled.

As an aside it may be mentioned, that a different temporal sulphur emission evolution occurred over east Asia (see Fig. 3): small emissions prior to 1950, a very large increase in emissions after 1950. This sulphur emission increase may have contributed to the cooling observed there and to the increasing pattern congruence.

It is interesting to note that in the sulphate experiment pattern congruence around 1910 was about as large as between 1970 and 1990. The reason for the decline in pattern congruence between 1910 and 1950 in the sulphur experiments may ultimately be the same as for the increase between 1950 and 1970: Overcooling by sulphates in the model, as discussed above with Mitchell et al. (1995).

The greenhouse gas-only signal, while weak throughout, peaks around 1940 (Santer et al., 1995a; their fig. 6) presumably because the observed warming produced a similar pattern as the one expected to result from a greenhouse gas increase. Indeed, the warming during the first half of the century was largest at higher latitudes, as expected from greenhouse gas only modelling experiments (see IPCC, 1992).

In any event, it appears as if the large increase in spatial congruence can be primarily related to the global cooling between 1950 and 1970. Whether that cooling can really be related to the effect of sulphates or whether it is just a chance spatial congruence is still a different matter in view of the fact that sulphur emissions increased steeply over some areas between 1910 and 1940 (see Fig. 3). This occurred without an apparent cooling impact on temperature (see discussion above) and it only occurred in summer and autumn. But it cannot be related to the action of greenhouse gases. The "anthropogenic effect on climate" alluded to by the authors in the title of their article must then be primarily related to the sulphate cooling effect on climate – if such an effect is realistic at all when one considers natural parameters which may have led to a similar cooling pattern as the modelled one. More light could be shed on the issue by realistically modelling the time dependent geographic evolution of sulphur emissions and accounting for natural factors. Furthermore, it is not clear why a sulphate effect should be most prominent in the autumn, as is apparent from Santer et al. (1995a). The authors do not convincingly discuss this issue.

Fingerprints in the modelled and observed vertical temperature structure of the atmosphere

The next piece of evidence cited in support of a human influence on the climate system deals with the vertical temperature structure of the atmosphere. Greenhouse theory predicts that, as a result of increasing greenhouse gas concentrations, the troposphere, that is the region between the surface and approximately 10km height should warm, whereas the stratosphere, that is the region between 10 and 40 km should cool.

This forms the basis for a fingerprint study by Karoly et al. (1994) in which a 'fingerprint' was defined as the zonal mean (averaged along a latitude circle) temperature change as a function of height and latitude. Observations were compared to a doubled CO_2 run. The authors find that there is a significant increase of a greenhouse signal in the observed data between 1963 and 1987. Two time periods were chosen to assess changes in this analysis, 1963–73 and 1978–88. The authors find that pattern correlation and pattern congruence both increase between 1963 and 1987 and that ENSO effects and stratospheric ozone depletion are unlikely to be responsible for the observed pattern changes.

There are several points to consider here. First, the modelled response of the vertical temperature structure of the atmosphere should indeed be a prime candidate for fingerprint studies, since it has some unique features: the ratio between low and high latitude warming at the surface (low warming rates at low latitudes, high warming rates at high latitudes) and the ratio between lower and upper tropospheric warming (large warming in the upper troposphere in low latitudes, low warming in the upper troposphere in higher latitudes), cooling in the stratosphere, and no pronounced latitudinal dependency (see Fig. 4).

Second, the time period chosen here is relatively short (only 15 years difference between both periods). This may be too short a period to detect and attribute a greenhouse gas fingerprint

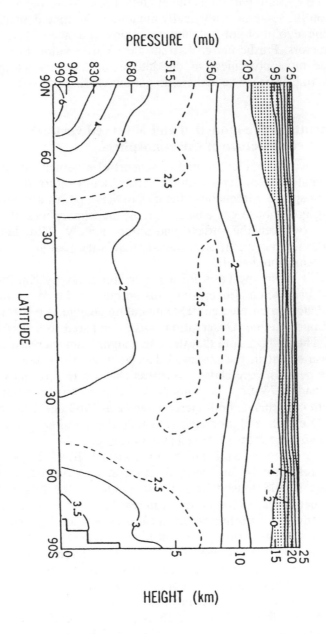

Figure 4: Zonally averaged temperature response of the atmosphere for the equilibrium climate for the doubling of atmospheric carbon dioxide. Units are degrees Celsius.

signal against the level of background noise. Finally, the significance of natural climate variability should be assessed.[2]

The observed pattern derived by Karoly et al. shows maximum warming in the middle troposphere of the southern hemisphere but also in the lower troposphere in the low northern latitudes, cooling in the stratosphere centred over southern high latitudes, but also in the upper troposphere of higher northern latitudes.

It may be noted in passing that different tropospheric temperature analyses exist which suggest that – in the northern hemisphere at least – maximum warming occurred in the upper tropical troposphere in recent decades (Weber, 1997).

As a result of natural fluctuations, the magnitude of any such trends in recent decades depends critically on the exact time period considered. A study probing for greenhouse fingerprints should involve a sensitivity analysis in which various time periods are considered to ensure that any conclusions drawn from it are not a result of a fortuitous coincidence: a greenhouse fingerprint should be a stable and not a transient feature of the climate system in recent decades.

Contrary to the claim of the authors, tropospheric warming between the two periods 1963–1973 and 1978–1988, which was found to be within model predictions, was to a great extent influenced by natural parameters, which led to a similar temperature pattern to the one expected from a greenhouse gas increase. There are two reasons for this.

First, the early years of that period were substantially influenced by the eruption of the volcano Mount Agung. The effects of a volcanic eruption include tropospheric cooling and stratospheric warming (see e.g. Angell, 1988). Any recovery from this response will produce a 'greenhouse' signal of tropospheric warming and stratospheric cooling.

Second, the later years of that period were influenced by several El Niño events, or large negative phases of the Southern Oscillation Index (SOI). The SOI was -.04 in 1963–1973 and -.49 in 1978–1988, significantly lower. El Niño events (periods of negative SOI) again lead to similar vertical temperature patterns as greenhouse warming: warming in the troposphere and cooling in the stratosphere, at least in the tropics (e.g. Reid et al., 1989). The

---

[2] On this issue see the article in this volume by Wiin-Nielsen and Wiin-Christensen.

magnitude of the trend, but also the pattern was therefore enhanced by natural factors.

The discrepancy between the vertical temperature pattern and the El Niño pattern found by the authors disappears when other data compilations (e.g. Weber, 1997) are considered, which – in the El Niño case – point to maximum warming in the upper tropical troposphere. However, that alone can also be expected from greenhouse warming and would in fact support the greenhouse scenario.

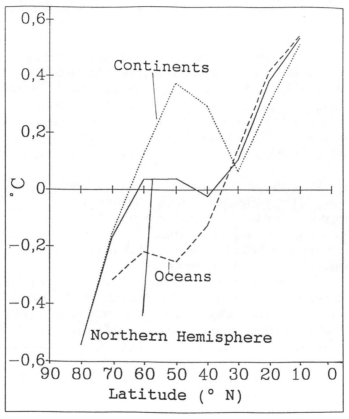

[Quelle Weber, Int. Journ. Climate, 1990]

Figure 5: Temperature departures in the troposphere (between altitudes 0-9km above sea level) of the Northern Hemisphere averaged between 1977-1986 as a function of latitude and separated by continents and oceans. The base period is 1951-1960

In the greenhouse scenario, on the other hand, there is only a very small latitudinal variation of integral tropospheric warming; that is, there is roughly the same amount of tropospheric warming near the equator and near the poles (see Fig. 4). In the El Niño scenario, by comparison, tropospheric warming is concentrated in the lower latitudes (0–30°), while the mid and higher latitudes may even experience a cooling. This is what has been observed between 1977 and 1987 (see e.g. Weber, 1990, and Fig. 5), almost exactly the same time period used by the authors. After 1987, the mid latitudes of the northern hemisphere experienced a dramatic warm-up (Angell, 1994; Weber, 1995), illustrating that trends may rapidly change as a function of the time frame considered.

In addition, it can be shown that tropospheric, in particular upper tropospheric, warming in the tropics has, in recent decades, been very closely related to variations of the SOI (Weber, 1997).

The conclusion of the authors that El Niño-Southern Oscillation (ENSO) events are not a significant contributor to the observed increasing fingerprint and that they exhibit a different pattern than those observed in recent decades, appears not to be well founded. Countervailing evidence abounds both in the observational and in the modelling arena (Kumar et al., 1994; Knutson and Manabe, 1994; Graham, 1995).

In the end it comes down to the natural variability issue: if natural variability is assumed to be low, in other words, if one assumes that there are no volcanic eruptions which may cool the climate by the same amount that greenhouse warming warms it, or El Niño events, which may warm it by a comparable amount, then one may conclude that the changes observed between 1963 and 1987 are indicative of greenhouse induced changes. This assumption is unwarranted.

The extension of the work analysed above probably is the chief witness for the statement that "the body of statistical evidence suggests....". It was referenced in the SAR as a Lawrence Livermore National Laboratory report and published in article form in July 1996, just in time for COP-2 (Santer et al., 1996). The timing may have been more than just coincidence.

What Santer et al. (1995b, 1996) did was simply take the Karoly et al. (1994) study and add modelled sulphate and stratospheric ozone depletion effects to it.

That makes it easy to analyse, because much of what has been said regarding the Karoly et al. (1994) study holds true here as well as the fact that the natural parameters may have been responsible for a similar magnitude and pattern of the warming observed between 1963 and 1987.

The two additional things to consider here are sulphates and stratospheric ozone depletion. Santer et al. (1996) conclude that the largest contribution to signal pattern strength is due to two factors: one, in the troposphere, the trend difference between northern and southern hemispheric warming (larger warming in the southern hemisphere due to lower sulphate concentrations) and two, the stratospheric–tropospheric trend difference (because of stratospheric cooling predicted under the greenhouse theory).

Regarding sulphates, we may remember what we concluded when analysing the sulphate studies of Mitchell et al. (1995) and Santer et al. (1995a). There is no discernible and consistent trend difference between the southern and the northern hemisphere surface air temperature record in recent decades – or in the last 100–130 years for that matter. Assuming the sulphate hypothesis is correct, there should be a consistent difference. This assumption is equally questionable.

Yet Santer et al. (1996) show that there is an interhemispheric difference in the troposphere. Well, there is in 1963–1987. Does that prove a sulphate impact? No, not really. Because 1963–1987 is just about the only period when such a difference exists in recent decades, following a tropospheric data compilation by Angell (1994). Beginning in 1965 – and through the early 1990s – the troposphere in the northern hemisphere warms more than in the southern hemisphere – increasing over time (see Fig 6). So much for the sulphate cooling effect. For the sulphate cooling effect to be real, the temperature difference should be consistent in time. (Michaels & Knappenberger, 1996; Weber, 1996).

The second point raised by Santer et al. (1996) is the increasing difference between tropospheric warming and stratospheric cooling, as expected from the greenhouse warming theory. When taking a closer look at tropospheric warming and stratospheric cooling in the period considered by Santer et al. (1996), some surprising results emerge. One, the stratosphere in the northern hemisphere did not cool at all in 1963–1987, at least not at mid-latitudes. Two, most of the cooling seen in the southern hemisphere stratosphere occurred after 1983, when temperatures there suddenly dropped by 2–3°C (see Fig. 7). That cooling might be associated with ozone depletion related to the Antarctic ozone hole – but it appears unrelated to greenhouse warming. So the largest contribution to that part of the fingerprint came from non-greenhouse causes (see also Ramaswamy et al., 1996).

The tropospheric warming itself has already been considered when we looked at Karoly et al. (1994). Natural parameters could be identified which produced a similar pattern of warming in the troposphere.

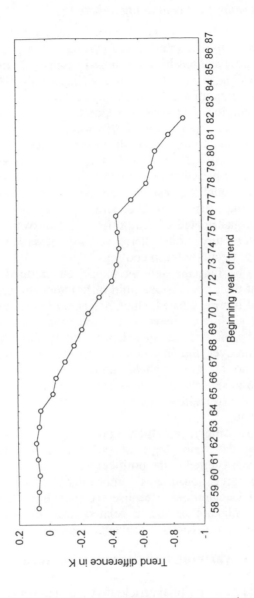

Figure 6: Tropospheric temperature trend differences between the mid-latitudes of the southern and northern hemisphere. Shown are the differences between trend (in k/dec) ending in 1992 and beginning in the year indicated. Negative values indicate larger warming in the northern hemisphere. Data source: Angell, Trends '93 (1994).

On balance, the evidence presented by Santer et al. (1995b, 1996) in favour of a human impact, then, does not look

83

compelling, except maybe for ozone-related cooling in the southern hemisphere stratosphere (Weber, 1996). That, however, is nothing new and has been discussed extensively in the scientific literature (Volk et al., 1996; Kiehl et al., 1988; Atkinson et al., 1989; Schwartzkopf and Ramaswamy, 1993).

From the fingerprinter's point of view, extending their analyses to the early and mid-1990s looks much more promising; there is now much more pronounced stratospheric cooling even in the northern hemisphere. Again, it is an open question whether that cooling is greenhouse gas or ozone related – or still natural variability. Modelling results seem to suggest, though, that the ozone cooling effect in the stratosphere by far outweighs greenhouse gas related cooling effects (Ramaswamy et al., 1996) and therefore any stratospheric cooling observed now is very likely due to ozone-induced cooling.

To be fair, the authors should be credited for expressly stating that their conclusions hold only under the assumption that no external forcing existed which has acted in the same manner as the perceived human impacts. On the other hand, that external forcing did exist, and climate scientists know about it.

Moreover, the only human impacts one could – debatably – discern so far are sulphate induced tropospheric and ozone induced stratospheric cooling – but no greenhouse gas induced warming. Yet greenhouse gases are the real issue in the climate change debate.

Surprisingly, and then again maybe not so surprisingly considering the weird logic of political processes, the human impacts claim is cited in the political documents demanding action to reduce greenhouse gas emissions (IPCC SPM, COP-2 Ministerial Declaration): Because we may have found a climate impact of sulphate or ozone related cooling, we have to cut greenhouse gas emissions to prevent a warming.

The rate of warming and the role of natural climate variability

The next and final article that has had some impact on the human impact claim is the one cited at the beginning, the work by Hegerl et al. (1994), which has, in the meantime, been published in a peer-reviewed journal (Hegerl et al., 1996). In this study, the impact of greenhouse gases alone on surface air temperature over the last 130 years is analysed applying a so-called optimum fingerprint approach. The optimal fingerprint is a specific statistical technique designed to maximise the signal-to-noise ratio

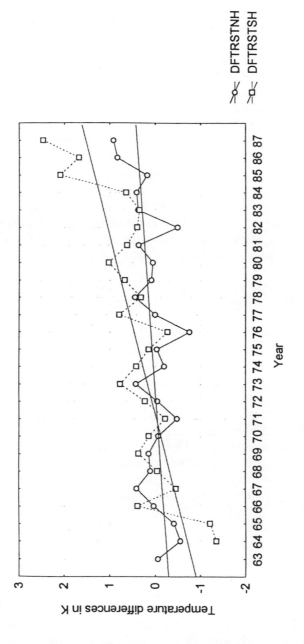

Figure 7: Tropospheric/stratospheric temperature differences in the northern and in the southern hemisphere between 1963 and 1987. Data source: Angell, Trends '93 (1994). The least squares linear trend is .97K/dec in the SH and .27K/dec in the NH.

by 'looking' for a pre-defined temperature change pattern. In the study, several ways are defined to look for that fingerprint, most of them comparing trends of observed patterns with modelled patterns of surface temperature change. The 'detection variables' in all cases show strong positive trends in recent decades, the largest contributor to those trends being the global mean temperature and not so much the warming pattern, a result which would be expected when recalling the CO_2 only experiment of Santer et al. (1995a).

In essence, what this study seems to tell us – when one attempts to see through the sophisticated statistical techniques deployed in the study – is that the *rate* of global temperature increase in the last 15-30 years has been higher than ever before and that it cannot entirely be explained by internal variability of the climate system. Therefore, it has to be partially due to the action of greenhouse gases (with an error probability of less than 5%).

Without dwelling on the more intricate statistical issues involved here, we will focus on three main questions: is modelled internal variability of the climate system the correct parameter to use when trying to establish the level of natural variability of the climate system, and estimating signal to noise ratios? Are the last 130 years sufficient to establish observed natural variability of the climate system? Can natural parameters be discounted as warming agents in recent decades?

A common thread running through all the studies analysed so far is the use of modelled internal variability of the climate system when establishing significance levels of observed changes. Modelled climate variability on decadal and century time scales is well known to be quite small (Manabe and Stouffer, 1996; Hegerl et al., 1994). One study, in which a climate modelling experiment was run for a 1000 model years (Manabe and Stouffer, 1996) concludes that the probability of a 0.5 °C global temperature increase was very small and much larger than modelled internal variability on the same time scale. Implicit conclusion: The temperature rise observed during the last 100 years must be due to 'unnatural' causes, probably meaning the greenhouse effect.

However, a temperature rise of 0.5 °C occurred between 1910 and 1950 alone, and it could not have been caused by the greenhouse effect, even if one believed present climate model predictions. Therefore, there must be natural climate variability – internal or non-greenhouse external – that is larger than the modelled internal variability of the climate system.

Further evidence that real, natural, climate variability is much larger than modelled internal variability comes from paleo-climate data and historic temperature reconstructions (see e.g. Lamb, 1988; Pfister, 1988), which indicates that peak-to-trough climate variations on century time scales may well be between 0.5 and 1.0 °C. Examples in the last 1000 years are the Medieval Warm Period and the Little Ice Age. On regional scales, a cooling did occur between the eighteenth and the nineteenth century which was almost as large as the warming between the nineteenth and the twentieth century (Wang and Wang, 1991; Weber, 1994; Böhm, 1992).

Therefore, one may conclude that the modelled internal variability of the climate system does not come close to representing the true observed variability of the climate system. The observed variability on the other hand is not only a result of internal variability, but of external, natural, forcing as well. Hence, when concluding that any observed signal is significantly larger than modelled variability, one has to make sure that this signal is not due to some natural external forcing before claiming man-made factors as a cause.

This appears to be a major shortcoming of all studies analysed so far and it is certainly one of the considerations which should lead us to be suspicious of any claim to anthropogenic warming.

Hegerl et al. (1994) additionally determined significance for their warming trends on the basis of observed temperature trends 1860–1990 adjusted for a modelled greenhouse warming trend. The underlying assumption is that 1860–1990 is representative of the true natural variability of the climate system. In the absence of global data before 1860, we cannot test this hypothesis.

One way to get an idea of natural variability before and after 1860 is to compare regional climate data. Relatively reliable regional instrumental data go back to the middle and the latter part of the eighteenth century, and in a few cases to the year 1700 or even slightly before (Manley, 1974).

To demonstrate the effect of time period selection, natural variability is estimated here for some sample European stations and two different time periods. To achieve a roughly 100 year period in both cases, the year 1880 is chosen as the dividing year between the early and the modern period. The modern post-1880 period has been adjusted for a greenhouse warming trend, in a similar fashion as in Hegerl et al. (1994). As an indicator for climate variability, the standard deviation (σ) has been calculated for annual and decadal averages. The results are shown in Table 1.

	BEFORE 1880 σ [°C]	AFTER 1880 σ[°C]	BEFORE 1880 σ_{10}[°C]	AFTER 1880 σ_{10}[°C]
BERLIN	.94	.78	.36	.24
CENENG	.63	.51	.31	.17
DEBILT	.76	.60	.30	.15
HPG	.87	.68	.37	.24
UPPSALA	1.01	.97	.39	.30
WARSAW	1.03	.80	.24	.25

σ   : Standard deviation of annual average temperature.
σ_{10} : Standard deviation of 10 year average temperatures. After
      1880 adjusted for Greenhouse warming trend.

Tab 1: European Climate Variations Before and After 1880

Who would have expected that climate variability was much smaller in the twentieth century than before? Particularly on decadal time scales, European climate was much more variable before 1880. The assumption that climate variations in the twentieth century (adjusted for a greenhouse warming trend) are an indicator of true variability is apparently not warranted. Therefore, climate variability may be much larger than assumed by Hegerl et al. (1994), and consequently, their trend significances much lower.

On the other hand, what appears to be true for Europe, may not to be true for the rest of the world. However, particularly on decadal time scales, the correlation between European and global temperatures is remarkably high, between 0.8 and 0.9 (Weber, 1994).

The close relation between European and global temperatures on decadal time scales even holds for the most recent past. The 10-year average 1986–1995 is at many European stations either the warmest or one of the warmest on record. Applying a similar trend analysis as Hegerl et al. (1994) to European temperature records, 15–30 year warming trends are large in the last 15 to 30 years – as in the global average. However, if one looks before 1860, which European records allow, warming rates as large or larger than those in the present have occurred before (see Fig. 8). This may have been the case with global averages as well, considering the close statistical relationship between

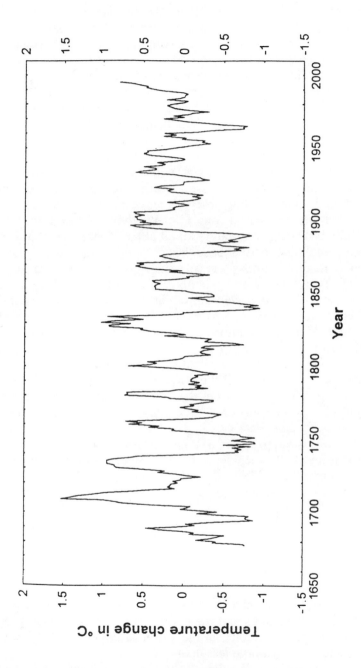

Figure 8: Temperature changes in Central England 1659-1996. Shown are changes over a 15-year period ending in the year indicated.

European and global averages. In that case, one could draw the conclusion, that even though present warming rates are indeed large by historical standards, even larger warming rates have been observed in the period before the one considered by Hegerl et al. (1994; 1996). Hence, only the restriction of the analysis by Hegerl et al. (1994) to the period after 1860 could have led to the conclusion, the most recent warming is larger than ever before observed and that it is larger than natural variability. Thus the implication of anthropogenic causes of that warming remains unproved.

Point three of this analysis will focus on the question of whether natural parameters can really be excluded as an explanation for the warming observed in recent decades.

Part of the answer was already given in the preceding paragraph, because if warming – albeit at a regional level – has in the pre-greenhouse period been larger than in the recent past, obviously natural factors do exist which may cause such a large warming. Therefore, natural parameters cannot be excluded per se.

But what do we know about identifiable natural parameters which may also have caused a warming in the most recent past? Volcanic eruptions cause a cooling in the troposphere, as, for example, after Mt. Agung in 1963, El Chichon in 1982 and Mt. Pinatubo in 1991, and could in relative terms only be responsible for a warming if the frequency of eruptions decreased during the period. This was not the case in recent decades. More frequent El Niño events, or negative phases of the SOI are a more likely warming candidate (see e.g. Angell, 1988; 1990). El Niño events, that is the appearance of a large warm water body over the eastern tropical Pacific, lead to worldwide temperature and climate anomalies, which are well documented and which have been studied extensively (see e.g. Yarnal, 1985; Quiroz, 1983; Namias, 1976). The impact of the SOI on global and regional temperatures can easily be determined statistically as is shown in Table 2.

It is worth mentioning that the early and mid-70s – the peak of global cooling – were characterised by strong 'anti' El Niño conditions, whereas in the early 1990s, pronounced El Niño conditions prevailed. Table 2 shows that about half the warming between the early 1970s and the early 1990s may statistically be attributed to SOI variations; in the lower latitudes (0–30°N) that fraction increases to a little less than two thirds.

Moreover, model calculations which analysed the impact of higher SSTs in the tropical Pacific were able to show that a similar spatial temperature structure to the observed one was reproduced (Graham, 1995; Kumar et al., 1994).

Average Tropospheric Temperatures in the last decades

	1971-1975	1989-1993
0-30°N	-.03°C	.45°C
0-90°N	-.14°C	.30°C

Statistical Contribution of SOI Variations to the Temperature Increase 1971-1993

0-30°N	.30°C
0-90°N	.23°C

Table 2. Impact of El Niño-Southern Oscillation Effects upon Tropospheric Temperatures in the Northern Hemisphere.

Of particular relevance in this context is the pattern of the calculated and observed response: cooling over the North Pacific, warming over the western North American continent, cooling over the eastern North American continent and warming over Siberia. Over the Atlantic and western Europe, the modelled El Niño response is weak.

From the discussion of the sulphate impact studies of Mitchell et al. (1995) and Santer et al. (1995a) one may recall that a similar warming/cooling pattern was found in the modelled response to sulphur emissions. Is the cooling over the North Pacific due to sulphur emissions or to a more frequent occurrence of El Niño events? At the very least one would suspect that the cooling over the Pacific and eastern North America is not entirely due to sulphates, and that there is a natural (El Niño) contribution as well (van Loon and Rogers, 1981; Namias, 1984).

Fluctuation of natural parameters which may be unrelated to the greenhouse effect are also implicated in explaining observed warming/cooling patterns in the studies by Wallace et al. (1995) and Hurrell (1995), who showed that those patterns are closely tied to circulation anomalies over the Pacific and Atlantic Oceans.

The cooling of the North Atlantic Ocean is generally tied to an intensified Icelandic low, which led to a strengthened north-westerly flow of cold air from the Canadian Arctic over the North Atlantic. The observed cooling in recent decades is in fact not restricted to the ocean, but encompasses the eastern Canadian Arctic, Greenland and the inner polar basin (Kahl et al., 1993).

91

Therefore, the ocean cooled primarily in response to atmospheric changes and probably not in response to changes in deep ocean dynamics, as suggested in the SAR (Kattenberg et al., 1996). The modelled response shows a warming over the Canadian Arctic and the higher latitudes as well, in contrast to observations – suggesting different causative mechanisms.

So-called teleconnection pattern studies have long suggested dynamical links between atmospheric circulation anomalies over one specific region and anomalies over different regions thousands of miles away (e.g. Namias, 1981; Wallace and Gutzler, 1981; Barnston and Livezey, 1987).

One of those patterns (Namias, 1981) points to a strong link between negative anomalies in the Greenland / Canadian Arctic region, positive anomalies over the western Atlantic, central Europe, eastern Siberia and negative anomalies over the eastern Mediterranean and the Middle East, a pattern which has frequently been observed in recent years and which undoubtedly contributed to the observed temperature distribution. Therefore, this pattern may not necessarily be linked to a sulphate cooling effect, but may instead be a natural fluctuation of the climate system.

Probably the most controversial natural factor in the climate change debate are solar climate links. The literature on the pros and cons of solar climate relationships is so extensive one could devote entire volumes to the topic (see e.g. NRC, 1994, references therein, and articles in this volume by Landscheidt and Posmentier et al.).

In short, the debate in the late nineties shapes up like this: There are very close statistical relationships between solar variations and various climate parameters – but no plausible and convincing physical explanation has been given, primarily because variations in solar energy flux are deemed too small to have any impact on climate. Scientists who favour the greenhouse hypothesis by and large are not too keen on pursuing solar climate links; the fact that statistical relationships between weak solar parameters and climate are so strong, but very weak between greenhouse gas concentrations and climate is particularly irksome to them.

Nonetheless, there seems to be agreement that the solar constant is not so constant after all and that solar variations have had some impact on climate in the past and should have some impact in the future as well (Lean and Rind, 1994; 1996; NRC,

1994; Haigh, 1996), even though the future impact vis-à-vis greenhouse gas should decline.

Part of the problem is that the exact value of the solar constant has been known for a short time only, namely since accurate satellite measurements became available. Scientists are hard-pressed to come up with similarly accurate numbers from say, 1860 or 1710: there were no satellites in orbit then and any estimate on the exact magnitude of solar irradiance must necessarily be much more inaccurate. Instead, as a proxy for solar activity, the sunspot number is often used, since it can be shown to vary with solar irradiance (e.g. Hoyt and Schatten, 1993).

Of the various solar irradiance models developed, most show that solar activity has been at its highest level in recent decades since sunspot observations began in the seventeenth century (e.g. Lean and Rind, 1996; Hoyt and Schatten, 1993; Landscheidt, 1995). The sunspot number has been at its highest level as well, the solar maxima in the late 1950s, around 1980 and 1990 are unprecedented.

In the light of presently available research it is somewhat speculative, but not unreasonable, to suspect that increasing solar activity has made a contribution to the warming observed in recent decades. It would, however, be very hard to quantify that contribution. Several attempts at quantifying (e.g. Hoyt and Schatten, 1993; Schlesinger and Ramankutty, 1992; Reid, 1991; Friis-Christensen and Lassen, 1991) would suggest that the solar contribution to the temperature increase during the last century could be anywhere between 25 and 80%, in some cases leaving little room for the greenhouse effect.

A possible physical link which might explain the seemingly large impact of small solar irradiance variations on terrestrial climate has been suggested by Svensmark and Friis-Christensen (1996). A good correlation has been found between global cloudiness and the cosmic ray flux. The cosmic ray flux varies with the intensity of the solar wind, which is strongly coupled with solar activity. Cosmic rays act as condensation nuclei thereby leading to cloudier conditions. Between solar minimum and solar maximum, cloud cover was observed to decrease by 3%. This may be translated into a radiative forcing variation of about 1.5 W m^{-2}, roughly the same amount as the cumulative greenhouse forcing since 1750.

In conclusion, it is fair to say that presently available research suggests that natural factors may at least explain part – if not all – of the warming and its spatial distribution in recent decades. As far as cooling by sulphates is concerned, the largest contributor to increasing pattern congruence must come from the areas of cooling over the North Atlantic, the North Pacific, and over the eastern Mediterranean. That cooling has in various studies been attributed to atmospheric circulation anomalies, leaving the role of sulphates open to debate.

Conclusions

When we now return to the question posed at the beginning, namely, do the studies cited in Chapter 8 of the SAR support the conclusion drawn at the end of Chapter 8 that the balance of the evidence suggests a discernible human impact on global climate, we would first of all have to differentiate which of the human impacts we are talking about. Taken at face value, the studies presented in Chapter 8, would, if anything, give some hints for ozone loss induced stratospheric cooling in the southern hemisphere and debatably some sulphate-induced cooling in the northern hemisphere. In contrast to that, the fingerprint case for a greenhouse gas induced warming is very weak to non-existent, except at first sight in Karoly et al. (1994) and Santer et al. (1996).

Upon closer examination, a number of problems become apparent, most of them related to the definition of natural variability, the time periods considered in the respective study and the role of natural parameters which may have caused similar climate trends and patterns as those ascribed to anthropogenic factors. A thorough analysis should rule out natural climate parameters before detection and attribution is claimed. This has not been done. Thus far, the fingerprint is still smudged.

The debate over the detection and attribution issue has detracted attention away from a more practical, and from a policy viewpoint a much more important issue: namely, how much of the observed warming could be attributed to the greenhouse effect, even if not all of the warming is due to natural factors? Even if attribution can be claimed, if the magnitude of true greenhouse warming is very small, too small to be of much practical relevance and much smaller than modelled, a climate change policy response would be vastly different – much less stringent – than a response to a more substantial warming.

References

Angell, J.K., 1988: Variations and trends in tropospheric and stratospheric global temperatures 1958–1987. *J. Climate*, 1, 1296–1313.

Angell, J.K., 1990: Variation in Global Tropospheric Temperature after Adjustment for the El Niño Influence, 1958–89. *Geophysical Research Letters*, 17, No. 8, 1.093–1.096.

Angell, J.K., 1994: Global hemispheric, and zonal temperature anomalies derived from radiosonde records. 636–673. In T. A. Boden, D. P. Kaiser, R.J. Sepanski, and F.W. Stoss (eds.), Trends '93: A Compendium of Data on Global Change. ORNL/CDIAC-65. Carbon Dioxide Information Analysis Center, Oak Ridge National Laboratory, Oak Ridge, Tenn., U.S.A. .

Atkinson, R. J., W. A. Matthews, P. A. Neumann & R. A. Plumb, 1989: Evidence of the mid-latitude impact of Antarctic ozone depletion. *Nature*, 340, 290–294.

Barnston, A.G. and R.E. Livezey, 1987: Classification, Seasonality and Persistence of Low-Frequency Atmospheric Circulation Patterns. *Monthly Weather Review*, Vol. 115, 1083–1125.

Böhm, R., 1992: Lufttemperaturschwankungen in Österreich seit 1775. Publ. 5, Zentralanstalt für Meteorol. und Geodyn., Wien, Austria.

Dignon J. and S. Hameed 1989: Global Emissions of Nitrogen and Sulphur Oxides from 1860 to 1980. *Journal of the Air Pollution Control Association*, 39, 180–186.

Friis-Christensen, C. und K. Lassen, 1991: Length of the Solar Cycle: An Indicator of Solar Activity Closely Associated with Climate. *Science*, 254, 698–700.

Graham, N. E., 1995: Simulation of Recent Global Temperature Trends. *Science*, 267, 666–671

Gschwandtner G., K. Gschwandtner, K. Eldridge, C. Mann and D. Mobley 1986: Historic Emissions of Sulphur and Nitrogen Oxides in the United States from 1900 to 1980. *Journal of the Air Pollution Control Association*, Vol. 36, No. 2, 139–149.

Hadley Centre, 1995: Modelling Climate Change 1860–2050 Bericht zur Ersten Vertragsstaatenkonferenz, Berlin, 27. März bis 7. April 1995, 13 Seiten. Hadley Centre, Bracknell, England.

Haigh, J. D., 1996: The Impact of Solar Variability on Climate. *Science*, 272, 981–984.

Hegerl, G. C., H. v. Storch, K. Hasselmann, B. D. Santer, U. Cubasch and P. D. Jones, 1994: Detecting Anthropogenic Climate Change with an Optimal Fingerprint Method. Max-Planck-Institut für Meteorologie, Report No. 142, 1–59.

Hegerl, G. C., H. v. Storch, K. Hasselmann, B. D. Santer, U. Cubasch and P. D. Jones, 1996: Detecting anthropogenic climate change with a fingerprint method. Max-Planck-Institut für Meteorologie, Report No. 168, 20 pp..

Hoyt, D.V., K.H. Schatten, 1993: A Discussion of Plausible Solar Irradiance Variations, 1700–1992. *Journal of Geophy. Res.*, Vol. 98. A11, 18,895–18,906.

Hurrell, J. W., 1995: Decadal Trends in the North Atlantic Oscillation: Regional Temperatures and Precipitation. *Science*, Vol. 269, 676-679

Jones P. D., S.C.B. Raper, R.S. Bradley, H.F. Diaz, P.M. Kelly and T.M.L. Wigley 1986a: Northern Hemisphere Surface Air Temperature Variations: 1851-1984. *Journal of Climate and Applied Meteorology*, Vol. 25, 161-179.

Jones, P. D., S.C.B. Raper and T.M.L. Wigley, 1986b: Southern Hemisphere Surface Air Temperature Variations: 1851-1984. *Journal of Climate and Applied Meteorology*, 25, 1.213-1.229.

Kahl J.D., D. J. Charlevoix, N.A. Zaitseva, R.C. Schnell and M. C. Serreze 1993: Absence of evidence for greenhouse warming over the Arctic Ocean in the past 40 years. *Nature*, Vol. 361, 335-337.

Karoly, D. J., J.A. Cohen, G.A. Meehl, J.F.B. Mitchell, A. H. Oort, R.J. Stouffer, R.T. Wetherald, 1994: An example of fingerprint detection of greenhouse climate change. *Climate Dynamics*, 10, 97-105.

Kattenberg, A., F. Giorgi, H. Grassl, G. A. Meehl, J. F. B. Mitchell, R. J. Stouffer, T. Tokioka, A. J. Weaver, T. M. L. Wigley, 1996: Climate Models – Projections of Future Climate. In : Climate Change 1995, 289-357, Cambridge University Press.

Kerr, R. A., 1995a: It's Official: First Glimmer of Greenhouse Warming seen. *Science*, Vol. 270, 1565-1567

Kerr, R. A., 1995b: Studies Say – Tentatively – That Greenhouse Warming Is Here. *Science*, Vol. 268, 1567-1568.

Kerr, R. A., 1995c: Study Unveils Climate Cooling Caused by Pollutant Haze. *Science*, Vol. 268, 802.

Kiehl, J. T., B. A. Boville & B. P. Briegleb, 1988: Response of a general circulation model to a prescribed Antarctic ozone hole. *Nature*, 332, 501-504.

Knutson, Th. R. and Syukuro Manabe, 1994: Impact of increased CO_2 on simulated ENSO-like phenomena. *Geophy. Res. Letters*, Vol. 21, No. 21, 2295-2298.

Kumar, A., A. Leetmaa, M. J., 1994: Simulations of Atmospheric Variability Induced by Sea Surface Temperatures and Implications for Global Warming. *Science*, Vol. 266, 632-634.

Lamb, H.H., 1988: Weather, Climate and Human Affairs. Routledge, London and New York, 364 pp.

Landscheidt, T., 1995: Global Warming or Little Ice Age ? *Journal of Coastal Research* Special Issue No. 17: Holocene Cycles: Climate, Sea Levels, and Sedimentation, pp. 371-382. [Reprinted in this volume.]

Lean, J. and D. Rind, 1994: Solar Variability Implications for Global Change. EOS, Transactions, *American Geophysical Union*, 75, No. 1, 4-7.

Lean, J. and D. Rind, 1996: The Sun and Climate. *Consequences* 2, No. 1, 27-36.

Manabe, S., and R. J. Stouffer, 1996: Low-Frequency Variability of Surface Air Temperature in a 1000-Year Integration of a Coupled Atmosphere-Ocean-Land Surface Model. *Journal of Climate* 9, 376-393.

Manley, G., 1974: Central England temperatures: monthly means 1659-1973. Quart. *J. Roy. Meteorol. Soc.*, 100, 389-405.

Mahsood, E., 1995: Climate panel confirms human role in warming, fights off oil states. *Nature*, 378, 524.

Michaels, P.J., T.C. Knappenberger, 1996: Human effect on global climate? *Nature*, 384, 522-524.

Mitchell, J.F.B., T.C. Johns, J.M. Gregory & S.F.B. Tett, 1995: Climate response to increasing levels of greenhouse gases and sulphate aerosols. *Nature*, Vol. 376, 501-504

Namias, 1976: Some statistical and synoptic characteristics associated with El Niño. *Journal of Oceanography* 6, 130-38.

Namias, J., 1981: Teleconnections of 700 mb height anomalies for the northern hemisphere. *Calcofi Atlas*, 29.

Namias, J., and D. R. Cayan, 1984: El Niño: Implications for Forecasting. Oceans 27, 41-47.

National Research Council, 1994: Solar Influences on Global Change.

Nature News, 1995: New IPCC report set to confirm earlier warming conclusions. *Nature*, Vol. 377, 189.

OECD Environmental Data Compendium 1995. OECD Publications, Paris.

Pfister, C., 1988: Klimageschichte der Schweiz 1525-1860. Verlag Paul Haupt, Bern, Schweiz.

Quiroz, 1983: Relationship among the stratospheric and tropospheric zonal flows and the Southern Oscillation. *Monthly Weather Review* 111, 143-54.

Ramaswamy et al., 1996: Fingerprint of ozone depletion in the spatial and temporal pattern of recent lower-stratospheric cooling. *Nature*, Vol. 382, 616-618.

Reid, Georg. C., Kenneth. S. Gage, and John R. McAfee, 1989: The Thermal Response of the Tropical Atmosphere to Variations in Equatorial Pacific Sea Surface Temperature. *Journal of Geophysical Research*, 94, D12, 14,705-14,716.

Reid, George C., 1991: Solar Total Irradiance Variations and the Global Sea Surface Temperature Record. *Journal of Geophysical Research*, Vol. 96, No. D2, 2835-2844.

Santer, B. D. Santer, K. E. Taylor, T. M. L. Wigley, J. E. Penner, P. D. Jones und U. Cubasch, 1995a: Towards the detection and attribution of an anthropogenic effect on climate. *Climate Dynamics*, 12, 77-100.

Santer, B. D., K. E. Taylor, T. M. L. Wigley, P. D. Jones, D. J. Karoly, J. F. B. Mitchell, A. H. Oort, J. E. Penner, V. Ramaswamy, M. D. Schwartzkopf, R. J. Stouffer & S. Tett,

1995b: A search for human influences on the thermal structure of the atmosphere. PCMDI-Report No. 27, Lawrence Livermore National Laboratory, 26 pp.

Santer, B. D., K. E. Taylor, T. M. L. Wigley, T. C. Johns, P. D. Jones, D. J. Karoly, J. F. B. Mitchell, A. H. Oort, J. E. Penner, V. Ramaswamy, M. D. Schwartzkopf, R. J. Stouffer & S. Tett, 1996: A search for human influences on the thermal structure of the atmosphere. *Nature*, Vol. 382, 39-46.

Schlesinger, M. E. & N. Ramankutty, 1992: Implications for global warming of intercycle solar irradiance variations. *Nature*, Vol. 369, 330-333.

Schwarzkopf, M. D. and Ramaswamy, V.,1993: Radiative Forcing due to Ozone in the 1980S: Dependence on altitude of Ozone change. *Geophys. Res. Letters*, Vol. 20, No. 2, 205-208.

Svensmark, H. and Friis-Christensen, E., 1996: Variation of cosmic ray flux and global cloud coverage – a missing link in solar-climate relationship. Invited paper presented at the COSPAR96 space science conference at the University of Birmingham, submitted to the *Journal of Atmospheric and Terrestrial Physics*.

Taylor, K. E. & J. E. Penner, 1994: Response of the climate systems to atmospheric aerosols and greenhouse gases. *Nature*, 369, 734-737.

Van Loon, H. and J.C. Rodgers 1981: The Southern Oscillation Part II. Associations with changes in the middle troposphere in the northern winter. *Mon. Wea. Rev.*, 109, 1163-1168.

Volk, C. M., J. W. Elkins, D. W. Fahey, R. J. Salawitch, G. S. Dutton, J. M. Gilligan, M. H. Proffitt, M. Loewenstein, J. R. Podolske, K. Minschwaner, J. J. Margitan, K. R. Chan, 1996: Quantifying Transport Between the Tropical and Mid-Latitude Lower Stratosphere. *Science*, Vol. 272, 1763-1768.

Wallace, J. M. and Gutzler, D. S., 1981: Teleconnections in the geopotential height field during the Northern Hemisphere winter. *Mon. Wea. Rev.*, 109,784-812.

Wallace, J.M., Y. Zhang, J.A. Renwick, 1995: Dynamic Contribution to Hemispheric Mean Temperature Trends. *Science*, Vol. 270, 780-783

Wang, S. W. and R.S. Wang, 1991: Little Ice Age in China. *Chinese Science Bulletin,* Vol. 36, No. 3, 217-220.

Weber, G.-R., 1990a: Spatial and temporal variations of sunshine in the Federal Republic of Germany. *Theor.Appl.Climatol.* 41, 1-9.

Weber, G.-R., 1990b: Tropospheric Temperature Anomalies in the Northern Hemisphere 1977-1986. *International Journal of Climatology,* 10, 3-19.

Weber, G.-R., 1994: Long-term European temperature variations between 1525 and the present. Proceedings of Air & Waste Management Association International Specialty Conference 'Global Climate Change: Science, Policy, and Mitigation Strategies', April 5-8, 1994, Phoenix, Arizona, 120-152.

Weber, G.-R., 1995: Seasonal and regional variations of tropospheric temperatures in the Northern Hemisphere 1976-1990', *International Journal of Climatology,* Vol. 15 (1995), S. 259-274.

Weber, G.-R., 1996: Human effect on global climate? *Nature,* 384, 522-524.

Weber, G.-R. 1997: Spatial and temporal variations of 300 hPa temperatures in the northern hemisphere between 1966 and 1993. *Int. Journal of Climatology,* Vol. 17, 1-15.

Yarnal, B.,1985: Extratropical teleconnections with El Niño / Southern Oscillation (ENSO) events. *Phys.Geography* 9, 315- 351.

Gerd-Rainer Weber

Gerd-Rainer Weber undertook undergraduate and graduate studies in atmospheric sciences at the Free University of Berlin, during which time he was a Fulbright and Indiana University Scholar. Further study in America gained him an M.Sc. degree in atmospheric sciences from the University of Michigan. He returned to the Free University of Berlin to study for his Meteorology PhD in conjunction with the Max-Planck-Institute of Aeronomy.

Since 1985, Dr Weber has been a scientist with the German Coal Mining Association. He is presently responsible for scientific research, analysis and consultancy in the field of the environmental impact of coal burning, particularly problems related to acid rain and global warming.

Since 1993 he has been the head of the environment section of the German Coal Mining Association, responsible for the supervision and co-ordination of research in those areas as financed by the coal industry. He is a member of various environmental working-groups within German industry and international agencies. He carries out independent research on climate-related issues, has had publications in the peer-reviewed literature, and made contributions to a number of conferences. His book on the greenhouse effect was published in both English and German editions.

The Spin on Greenhouse Hurricanes

Robert C. Balling, Jr.
Office of Climatology and Department of Geography
Arizona State University
Tempe, Arizona 85287 USA

Summary

News reports of hurricanes anywhere around the world are often accompanied by statements mentioning global warming, the greenhouse effect, and the anthropogenic influence on climate. Somehow, the public has been convinced that the future will include an increasing number of hurricanes of greater intensity that will certainly do more and more damage throughout the world. But as with so many other elements in the greenhouse debate, the theoretical and empirical evidence is not very supportive of this claim. The overwhelming balance of evidence argues that the greenhouse effect will suppress the number and intensity of hurricanes in the future.

The January 22, 1996 cover of *Newsweek* showed a man walking through the whiteout of a snowstorm, and the cover curiously proclaimed 'The Hot Zone: Blizzards, Floods & Hurricanes: Blame Global Warming.' To emphasize the point, 'Hot' and 'Global Warming' appeared in bright red letters blaring through the white background of blowing snow. News reports of hurricanes (also called typhoons or tropical cyclones) anywhere around the world are often accompanied by statements mentioning global warming, the greenhouse effect, and the anthropogenic influence on climate. The media appear to be convinced that the future will include an increasing number of hurricanes of greater intensity that will certainly do more and more damage throughout the world. Concerns about hurricanes are now added to those we have regarding future heat stress, sea level rise, droughts, pestilence, crop failures, water shortages, wildfires, and all the other components of the 'greenhouse disaster'. This prediction is especially scary given the fact that hurricanes are among the most devastating natural disasters that affect many parts of the world. Accordingly, suggestions of an increase in hurricane activity deserve critical analysis by scientists and policymakers alike.

What is most surprising about the claims regarding the increasing number and intensity of hurricanes in the greenhouse world is the general lack of theoretical or empirical evidence in support of the claim. Much of the evidence we have to date argues against a link between global warming and increased hurricane activity. International scientific bodies have divorced themselves from the popularised prediction, and within recent months research has begun to show that our future may have fewer hurricanes of less intensity potentially doing less damage than ever before.

Like so many other elements of the greenhouse debate, the theoretical and empirical evidence does not seem to matter at all to some individuals interested in spreading the gloom and doom of global warming. I spent nearly one hour with the *Newsweek* authors explaining to them all that will follow in this chapter, but despite this discussion, the *Newsweek* clan planned a cover story in which global warming is blamed for hurricanes. This was not a matter of confusion regarding a complex scientific issue – I believe that *Newsweek* chose to ignore the facts and present the scariest possible story regarding our future and global warming.

Building the Link

If the observational and theoretical evidence is largely against a linkage between greenhouse gases, global warming, and the intensification of hurricane activity, one may fairly question how the linkage became such a permanent pillar in the global warming apocalypse. A rather amazing set of circumstances may be behind any fear we now have for a future of hurricane destruction.

In 1986, a noted hurricane scientist at M.I.T. named Kerry Emanuel published a highly technical and complex paper in the prestigious *Journal of the Atmospheric Sciences* dealing with the air-sea interactions and hurricane activity (Emanuel, 1986). In the article, Emanuel showed that if the sea-surface temperature falls below approximately 26°C, intense hurricanes become a physical impossibility. The cooler sea-surface temperatures would strengthen the inversion that exists in the trade winds of the subtropical to tropical latitudes, thereby limiting the growth of convective clouds in the hurricane system. Emanuel further showed that the intensity of a hurricane has a well-defined upper limit that is governed, in part, by the degree of thermodynamic disequilibruim between the atmosphere and the underlying ocean. In simple terms, a warmer sea-surface could theoretically increase the upper limit of a storm's intensity. Only a few storms actually approach this theoretical upper limit, but those storms turn out to be the most destructive and dangerous. Whether or not he realized it at the time, Emanuel had set a foundation for one of the more interesting misconceptions in the greenhouse debate.

This 1986 publication set the stage for several more important papers by Emanuel that would ultimately have a large impact on the greenhouse link to increased hurricane activity. The following year, Emanuel published another article in the *Journal of the Atmospheric Sciences* on the dependence of hurricane activity on climate (Emanuel, 1987). He showed that a numerical model perturbed by an increase in greenhouse gases would increase the disequilibrium between the ocean surface and the overlying atmosphere, and the theoretical upper limit of storm intensity would increase. This is not to say that the world would see more hurricanes or even more intense hurricanes, only that the upper limit of intensity could increase. For a 3°C increase in sea surface temperatures, the potential destructive power, as measured by the square of the wind speed, of storms approaching this theoretical limit could increase by 40 to 50%. Emanuel acknowledged from the outset that there are many reasons to be sceptical about his conclusions regarding this limit of storm intensity, particularly as this value is determined for future climatic conditions.

Several more papers in 1988 firmly set the stage for the inclusion of hurricanes into all future gloomy greenhouse predictions. A third paper by Emanuel in the *Journal of the Atmospheric Sciences* further developed the linkage between the upper limit of storm intensity and the warming occurring in the atmosphere (Emanuel, 1988a). Very importantly, this third paper introduced the rather snappy term 'hypercane' into the vocabulary of the atmospheric scientists. Not many people understood that Emanuel was talking about the upper limit of storm intensity, and he suggested with a warming of the sea surface of 6°C to 10°C (and with conditions in the lower stratosphere held constant), a supersized ultra-powerful hypercane becomes a theoretical possibility. No computer model ever predicted a greenhouse-induced temperature rise of 6°C for the tropical and subtropical sea surfaces that spawn hurricanes, but nonetheless, Emanuel had produced some interesting and valuable information about the physics of hurricane development and maintenance. These ideas were presented to a more popular audience in a paper he prepared for the *American Scientist* (Emanuel, 1988b), and not surprisingly, more people learned about the hypercane. By the summer of 1988, a world-class scientist at a first-rate institution had published articles in the finest journals that provided a linkage between atmospheric concentrations of greenhouse gases, global warming, and the development of these extraordinary hypercanes.

Other scientists also published articles in 1988 that were in agreement with the work of Emanuel (e.g., Merrill, 1988). In addition, Hobgood and Cerveny (1988) used a numerical hurricane model to simulate conditions during the height of an ice age, and they found a significant reduction in the intensity of the storms that developed in the model. If hurricanes weaken in ice age conditions, it is probable that they strengthen during a time of increased planetary temperature. The summer of 1988 also happened to be the time when the greenhouse effect and global warming made headline news day after day following a series of weather-related disasters. The summer of 1988 saw a severe drought in the south-eastern United States, the drying up of the Mississippi River, record breaking heatwaves, and wildfires in the American West (including the Yellowstone fires). All of these events followed the famous 23 June 1988 statement by James Hansen to Congress that scientists are '99% certain' that the anthropogenic greenhouse effect was having an impact on the global climate system. If the linkage between greenhouse effect and hurricanes needed a boost, it got one in September 1988 when nature presented us with the storm of the century.

North Americans had suffered through that summer, and the greenhouse effect was the culprit many of us blamed for our climate problems. Just as things were quietening down, a tropical storm named Gilbert appeared in September south of the Virgin Islands. Unlike other storms of the that hurricane season, Gilbert grew at an alarming rate, and its centre pressure dropped to 885 millibars which was the lowest pressure ever recorded for a hurricane in the Western Hemisphere. Winds in Gilbert were sustained at 280 km/hr (175 mph) as it smashed into the area around Cancún in the Yucatán of Mexico. Gilbert then headed north and arrived in southern Texas on September 16th; prayers for rain to end the drought were more than answered as Gilbert died in the interior of the United States.

Suddenly, the image of hurricanes, or even hypercanes, became part of our vision of the greenhouse world. While the greenhouse effect was so much a part of the public mindset, this enormous hurricane came along to confirm our worst fears about the future. Emanuel's work was brought into the discussion as proof that solid theoretical and empirical arguments existed linking global warming to super-size hurricanes. Fear-mongering became easy for anyone selling the greenhouse scare – the proof was before our eyes as we saw the incredible images of destruction associated with Hurricane Gilbert. If the events in 1988 were not sufficiently convincing, Hurricane Hugo struck the south-eastern coast of the United States in the following year to end all scepticism. People came to believe that hurricanes were increasing in intensity, magnitude, areal extent, duration, and ability to devastate our coastlines.

Bookstores and news-stands were suddenly filled with new issues proclaiming the coming disaster that would be driven in part by the increase in hurricane damage. Those members of the media less prone to hysteria looked for a credible source for comment on the likelihood of future hurricane activity. The governing council of the American Meteorological Society and the Board of Trustees of the University Corporation for Atmospheric Research (1988) issued a policy statement suggesting that greenhouse-induced global warming over the next 50 years will probably lead to "a higher frequency and greater intensity of hurricanes." By the end of the 1980s, the public must have been convinced that the scientific community was reasonably certain of this prediction, and, as we have seen, there were apparently many good reasons to believe in a coming hurricane-driven set of disasters. Anyone could, for whatever reason, construct a powerful case that humans were facing a world of greenhouse-related perils, including the probable threat from the coming hurricanes and hypercanes.

The Debate Begins

As with so many components in the greenhouse debate, the hurricane story might seem an open and shut case. Emanuel gave us theoretical reasons to expect an increase in hurricane activity given the build-up of greenhouse gases, he gave us an easy to remember and scary new name (hypercanes), the world seemed to be warming, and Hurricanes Gilbert and Hugo appeared to provide the final proof. However, in accordance with normal scientific procedure, some people began to question this simple interpretation. Some scientists understood that Kerry Emanuel never made a prediction of increased hurricane activity, but rather provided a theoretical discussion of the upper limit of hurricane intensity given a very large increase in sea surface temperatures. Within the community of scholars that knew the most about hurricanes and understood what Emanuel was saying, the public proclamations regarding the prediction of increased hurricane activity, were treated with caution.

In 1990, three different articles appeared in the professional literature that made no headlines in popular outlets, but raised serious doubts about the notion that hurricane activity was on the rise. Noted hurricane scientist William Gray published an article in *Science* dealing with the landfall of intense hurricanes in the United States and its relation to rainfall in West Africa. Within that article, Gray revealed that Atlantic hurricane activity over the period 1970-1987 was less than half of the activity observed for the period 1947-1969. The greenhouse gas concentration was going up exponentially, and yet Gray found that hurricanes were not showing the expected increase in number or intensity, but rather a decrease in overall activity.

Another research project was published in 1990 in *Meteorology and Atmospheric Physics* by a band of greenhouse sceptics at Arizona State University. This author worked with Sherwood Idso and Randall Cerveny on a research project that ultimately challenged the prediction for increasing hurricane numbers and intensities in the greenhouse world. Idso et al. (1990) gathered hurricane data for the central Atlantic, the east coast of the United States, the Gulf of Mexico, and the Caribbean Sea for the period 1947-1987. We felt that data prior to 1947 would be unreliable and potentially biased from hurricane assessment procedures used prior to the end of the Second World War. We carefully collected information on the number of hurricanes observed each year in the study area, the number of days with hurricanes, and the number of storms within various hurricane intensity categories. Rather than assess trends in these hurricane variables over the 41-year period, Idso et al. compared the hurricane data to estimates of the surface temperature in the Northern Hemisphere. We recognized that the Northern Hemisphere had shown considerable variation (nearly 1°C) in temperature over the 1947-1987 period, and wondered how hurricanes had responded to these observed temperature variations.

Idso et al. (1990, p. 261) found that "there is basically no trend of any sort in the number of hurricanes experienced in any of the four regions with respect to variations in temperature." The number of hurricane days was negatively related to the Northern Hemispheric temperatures; warmer years produced the lowest numbers of hurricane days while the cooler years had above-average numbers of hurricane days. The number of storms within the various intensity classes was also inversely correlated with the hemispheric temperature values (Figure 1). Idso et al. (1990, p. 262) examined the trends with different intensity classes and concluded: "For global warming on the order of one-half to one degree Centigrade, then, our analyses suggest that there would be no change in the frequency of occurrence of Atlantic/Caribbean hurricanes, but that there would be a significant decrease in the intensities of such storms."

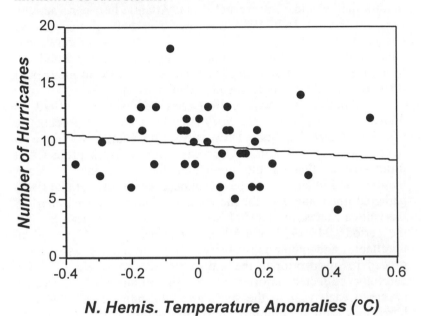

Figure 1. Number of Atlantic/Caribbean hurricanes verses northern hemispheric near-surface air temperature anomalies (°C) for each year from 1948 to 1987.

The Idso et al. work had some impact on the debate, but was never published in non-specialist literature. A few critics pointed to a potentially damaging aspect of their research – in an 'Acknowledgement' in the article, Idso et al. thanked the president of Cyprus Minerals Company for financial support for the project. Funding from many other sources (e.g., National Science Foundation, Environmental Protection Agency, National Oceanic and Atmospheric Administration) would have been fine, but funding from a coal mining company led to concerns that the results might be unreliable. Nonetheless, another article had been added to the scientific literature with evidence arguing against the popular belief that hurricanes should be blamed on global warming.

More research appeared in 1990 that raised doubts on the hurricane issue. Broccoli and Manabe (1990) published an article entitled 'Can existing climate models be used to study anthropogenic changes in tropical cyclone intensity?' When they allowed certain cloud-related feedbacks to be included in their numerical modelling experiments, they noted a 10-15% reduction in the number of days with hurricanes for a doubling of carbon dioxide. Their numerical simulation with cloud feedbacks suggested a reduction in hurricane number and/or duration for a world of higher concentrations of greenhouse gases. Broccoli and Manabe noted that their results were slightly unstable and highly dependent upon how they represented cloud processes within the model.

A pillar of the greenhouse scare was not likely to collapse given the evidence presented in these three articles. However, 1990 also brought the world the first scientific assessment from the Intergovernmental Panel on Climate Change (IPCC, 1990). In the 'Policymakers' Summary', we are told "climate models give no consistent indication whether tropical storms will increase or decrease in frequency or intensity as climate changes; neither is there any evidence that this has occurred over the past few decades." However, by the end of 1990, the issue of hurricanes and climate change had truly become a part of the heated debate.

Ebb and Flow in the 1990s

Throughout the 1990s, articles have appeared in major journals supporting and challenging the prediction of increased hurricane activity in the greenhouse world. In an article dealing with impacts on tropical forests, O'Brien et al. (1992) assumed that doubling carbon dioxide would increase tropical sea surface temperatures from 1°C to 4°C and double the number of hurricanes, increase their strength by 40-60%, and extend the hurricane season. Although their interest was clearly on the forests, their acceptance of the estimates of hurricane changes had the effect of adding weight and credibility to the claims. In addition, research by Ryan et al. (1992) suggested that areas conducive to hurricane generation could expand substantially in a warming world, although they fully acknowledged that their results gave an overestimation of the area of cyclogenesis.

Haarsma et al. (1993) used an 11-layer global general circulation model (GCM) coupled with an ocean model and found that a doubling of the concentration of greenhouse gases would increase the frequency of hurricanes by 50%, increase the mean intensity of the storms by 20%, and increase the number of intense hurricanes developing in the greenhouse world. Conversely, Landsea (1993) reported that the intensity of Atlantic hurricanes has been decreasing since the middle of this century; Landsea carefully screened his data to remove known biases, and the decreasing trend remained an identifiable pattern in the intensity estimates (Figure 2).

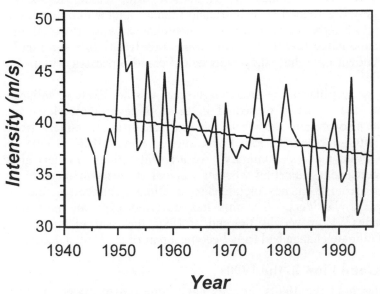

Figure 2. Time series of Atlantic basin mean intensity (m/s). as determined from maximum sustained wind speeds of all hurricanes, in each year from 1944 to 1995 (from Landsea et al., 1996).

Eight scientists (Lighthill et al., 1994) collaborated on a major review article entitled 'Global climate change and tropical cyclones' that appeared in the *Bulletin of the American Meteorological Society* in 1994. The authors took two different approaches, but both led to the conclusion that "even though the possibility of some minor effects of global warming on tropical cyclone frequency and intensity cannot be excluded, they must effectively be 'swamped' by large natural variability." This is hardly an endorsement for the idea that any future increases in hurricanes can be expected or blamed on the build-up of greenhouse gases.

One approach taken by Lighthill et al. involved an examination of a widely accepted list of conditions for permitting hurricane formation and development. The list includes some simple conditions such as a sea-surface temperature above 26°C, distance from the equator of at least 5° of latitude, and fairly high relative humidity levels surrounding the storm. Other entries on the list dealt with more complex conditions: the vertical temperature structure of the atmosphere, the change in wind velocity with height, and horizontal rotation of the system. Their analyses led to the conclusion that we should not expect any changes in hurricane frequency and intensity as a direct result of changing sea surface conditions. The authors point out that there are many unknown variables and that indirect effects could occur, but they found most impacts of rising sea surface temperature to be self-limiting.

Lighthill et al. also examined the hurricane activity data since 1944 in the Atlantic and since 1970 in the Pacific. The authors noted great year-to-year variability in the hurricane data, but they could not find evidence to link hemispheric temperatures to variations in hurricane activity. Not surprisingly, their article enlivened the debate on the hurricane question. Emanuel (1995) responded and questioned the Lighthill evaluation, arguing that both the basic physics and the empirical records of hurricane activity suggest that warming in the tropical oceans would be accompanied by an increase in the limiting intensity of actual hurricanes. Broccoli et al. (1995) questioned the pessimistic view of Lighthill et al. regarding the use of numerical climate models in this debate, and suggested that current and future simulations hold enormous promise in providing answers to the questions surrounding future tropical storms.

Lennart Bengtsson of Germany's Max Planck Institut für Meteorologie was one of the members of the Broccoli et al. team that commented on the Lighthill et al. review article. One year later, Bengtsson et al. (1996) published a paper in *Tellus* entitled 'Will greenhouse gas-induced warming over the next 50 years lead to a higher frequency and greater intensity of hurricanes?' Their high-resolution numerical simulations with a coupled ocean-atmosphere model showed that greenhouse-induced changes would weaken the Hadley circulation that dominates the tropics but would strengthen the upper-level westerlies in the vicinity of developing hurricanes. When compared with the present-day global distribution and seasonality of hurricanes, they found no changes for a doubling of greenhouse gases. However, the number

111

of hurricanes in the Northern Hemisphere fell from 56.2 storms per year in the present-day climate simulation (the observed value from 1958-1977 is 54.6) to 42.0 storms per year in the doubled CO_2 case. In the Southern Hemisphere, the number of hurricanes dropped from 26.8 in the present-day model run (24.5 is the observed value) to only 11.6 storms per year. Their results on intensity were less conclusive, but they did find a tendency for reduced wind speeds in the doubled CO_2 model simulations.

Another article by Landsea et al. (1996) confirmed the view that hurricane frequency and intensity were not increasing over the past five decades. Landsea et al. examined Atlantic hurricanes from 1944, when aircraft reconnaissance began in the Atlantic, to the present. They found that "a long-term (five decade) downward trend continues to be evident primarily in the frequency of intense hurricanes. In addition, the mean maximum intensity (i.e. averaged over all cyclones in a season) has decreased." A plot of the mean intensity (Figure 2) clearly shows this downward trend during a time of greatest build-up of greenhouse gases. Landsea et al. were fully aware that hurricanes occur in other ocean basins, but the data quality problems from other parts of the world preclude similar analyses from other locations.

This downward trend in the Atlantic hurricane basin over the past five decades is certainly interesting, but it raises the question about trends prior to the 1940s. Hard evidence is difficult to find for storms that moved through the Atlantic prior to the World War II. However, Karl et al. (1995, 1996) examined records of the number and intensity of hurricanes that reached the continental United States over the past century. Their research showed that the number of hurricanes making landfall in the United States has decreased from the 1940s through the 1980s, but their records also showed an increase in storms in the first half of the record (Figure 3). Over the twentieth century, no overall trend was discernible in the records. Elsner et al. (1996) looked at Atlantic hurricanes in the tropics from 1896-1990, and they noted a drop in these tropical hurricanes in the 1960s. The trend in tropical hurricanes was clearly downward during the past 50 years of most reliable records.

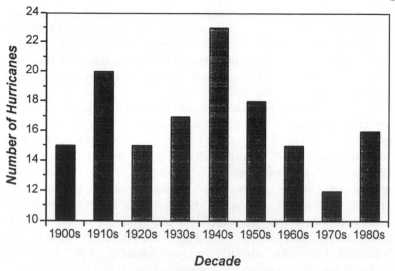

Figure 3. Number of hurricanes making landfall in the conterminous United States (from Karl et al., 1995, 1996).

The second scientific assessment of the Intergovernmental Panel on Climate Change was published in 1996 (IPCC, 1996), and once again, this international body addressed the issue of increasing hurricane activity in the next century. In the Technical Summary (p. 44), the IPCC group states "Although some models now represent tropical storms with some realism for present day climate, the state of the science does not allow assessment of future changes." This is hardly a ringing endorsement for the popular claim that we should blame global warming for hurricanes.

The Future

As we have seen in this section, a popular view has developed that the build-up of greenhouse gases will cause the sea surface and atmospheric temperatures to rise, and that this will result in an increase in the number and intensity of damaging hurricanes around the world. But as with so many other elements in the greenhouse debate, the theoretical and empirical evidence is not very supportive of this claim. Indeed, there is plenty of evidence to argue that the greenhouse effect will suppress hurricane activity.

In terms of direct effects, the information we have today does not predict any increase in the number of hurricanes in the future. Similarly, the mean intensity of the hurricanes that develop is not likely to increase. Emanuel's research has survived a decade of debate, and should there be a substantial warming in the tropical sea surface, the upper limit of hurricane intensity probably will rise, and, over a long time period, a few very powerful hurricanes may develop.

A compounding factor exists that may make detection of any changes more difficult than ever. It is well known that inter-annual variations in El Niño and La Niña have a significant impact on hurricane activity (Gray, 1984). During the El Niño periods with warm water off the Pacific coast of South America, the upper-level winds over the Atlantic increase, hurricane development and maintenance are inhibited, and the number of hurricanes as well as hurricane days are reduced. Oppositely, the cold water phase, called La Niña, tends to be associated with increased hurricane activity in the Atlantic. The overriding problem here is that Meehl and Washington (1996) have presented results from climate model simulations showing that an increase in the atmospheric concentration of greenhouse gases could lead to climatic anomalies in the tropical Pacific that are similar to the quasi-periodic (and natural) El Niño events. This finding further complicates the problem of untangling natural variations in hurricane activity from the effects of humans increasing the concentration of greenhouse gases in the atmosphere.

More research will provide better answers to these and other related questions – the month-to-month information flow in the greenhouse debate gives it a flavour unlike many similar debates in science. But if your insurance company raises your rates in the name of increased hurricane risk, get sceptical, and get the facts. It is easy to go along with the popular view as presented by *Newsweek*, but in the end, there is little reason to expect an increase in hurricane activity in the next century.

References

AMS Council and UCAR Board of Trustees, 1988: The changing atmosphere – challenge and opportunities. *Bulletin of the American Meteorological Society,* 69, 1434-1440.

Bengtsson, L., M. Botzet, and M. Esch, 1996: Will greenhouse gas-induced warming over the next 50 years lead to a higher frequency and greater intensity of hurricanes? *Tellus,* 48A, 57-73.

Broccoli, A.J., and S. Manabe, 1990: Can existing climate models be used to study anthropogenic changes in tropical cyclone intensity? *Geophysical Research Letters,* 17, 1917-1920.

Broccoli, A.J., S. Manabe, J.F.B. Mitchell, and L. Bengtsson, 1995: Comments on 'Global climate change and tropical cyclones': Part II. *Bulletin of the American Meteorological Society,* 76, 2243-2245.

Elsner, J.B., G. S. Lehmiller, and T. B. Kimberlain, 1996: Objective classification of Atlantic hurricanes. *Journal of Climate,* 9, 2880-2888.

Emanuel, K. A., 1986: An air-sea interaction theory for tropical cyclones. Part I: Steady-state maintenance. *Journal of the Atmospheric Sciences,* 43, 585-604.

Emanuel, K. A., 1987: The dependence of hurricane intensity on climate. *Nature,* 326, 483-485.

Emanuel, K. A., 1988a: The maximum intensity of hurricanes. *Journal of the Atmospheric Sciences,* 45, 1143-1156.

Emanuel, K. A., 1988b: Toward a general theory of hurricanes. *American Scientist,* 76, 370-379.

Emanuel, K. A., 1995: Comments on 'Global climate change and tropical cyclones': Part I. *Bulletin of the American Meteorological Society,* 76, 2241-2243.

Gray, W.M., 1984: Atlantic seasonal hurricane frequency. Part 1: El Niño and 30 mb quasi-biennial oscillation influences. *Monthly Weather Review,* 112, 1649-1668.

Gray, W.M., 1990: Strong association between West African rainfall and U.S. landfall of intense hurricanes. *Science,* 249, 1251-1256.

Haarsma, R.J., J.F.B. Mitchell, and C.A. Senior, 1993: Tropical disturbances in a GCM. *Climate Dynamics,* 8, 247-257.

Hobgood, J. S., and R.S. Cerveny, 1988: Ice-age hurricanes and tropical storms. *Nature,* 333, 243-245.

Idso, S.B., R.C. Balling Jr., and R.S. Cerveny, 1990: Carbon dioxide and hurricanes: Implications of Northern Hemispheric warming for Atlantic/Caribbean storms. *Meteorology and Atmospheric Physics,* 42, 259-263.

IPCC: Houghton, J.T., G.J. Jenkins, and J.J. Ephraums (eds.), 1990: *Climate Change: The IPCC Scientific Assessment.* Cambridge: Cambridge University Press.

IPCC: Houghton, J.T., L.G. Meira Filho, B. A. Callander, N. Harris, A. Kattenberg, and K. Maskell (eds.), 1996: *Climate Change 1995: The Science of Climate Change.* Cambridge: Cambridge University Press.

Karl, T.R., R.W. Knight, D. R. Easterling, and R.G. Quayle, 1995: Trends in U.S. climate during the twentieth century. *Consequences,* 1, 3-12.

Karl, T.R., R.W. Knight, D. R. Easterling, and R.G. Quayle, 1996: Indices of climate change for the United States. *Bulletin of the American Meteorological Society,* 77, 279-292.

Landsea, C.W., 1993: A climatology of intense (or major) Atlantic hurricanes. *Monthly Weather Review,* 121, 1703-1713.

Landsea, C.W., N. Nicholls, W. M. Gray, and L. A. Avila, 1996: Downward trends in the frequency of intense Atlantic hurricanes during the past five decades. *Geophysical Research Letters,* 23, 1697-1700.

Lighthill, J., G. Holland, W. Gray, C. Landsea, G. Craig, J. Evans, Y. Kurihara, and C. Guard, 1994: Global climate change and tropical cyclones. *Bulletin of the American Meteorological Society,* 75, 2147-2157.

Meehl, G.A., and W.M. Washington, 1996: El Niño-like climate change in a model with increased atmospheric CO_2 concentrations. *Nature,* 382, 56-60.

Merrill, R.T., 1988: Environmental influences on hurricane intensification. *Journal of the Atmospheric Sciences,* 45, 1678-1687.

O'Brien, S. T., B. P. Hayden, and H.H. Shugart, 1992: Global climatic change, hurricanes, and a tropical forest. *Climatic Change,* 22, 175-190.

Ryan, B.F., I.G. Watterson, and J.L. Evans, 1992: Tropical cyclone frequencies inferred from Gray's yearly genesis parameter: Validation of GCM tropical climates. *Geophysical Research Letters,* 19, 1831-1834.

Robert Balling

Dr Robert C. Balling, Jr. is currently Director of the Office of Climatology at Arizona State University. Over the last five years, Dr Balling has been heavily involved in the greenhouse debate. He has published over 70 articles in the professional scientific literature, received over $1,000,000 in research grants, presented lectures throughout the United States and more than a dozen foreign countries, and appeared in a number of scientific documentaries and news features. He is presently serving as a climate consultant to the United Nations, the World Meteorological Organisation, and the Intergovernmental Panel on Climate Change. Dr Balling's book on his research is entitled *The Heated Debate: Greenhouse Predictions Versus Climate Reality.*

What to do about Greenhouse Effects: Control of Atmospheric CO_2 through Ocean Fertilisation: An Alternative to Emission Controls

S. Fred Singer
President
The Science & Environmental Policy Project
Virginia
USA

Summary

Ocean fertilisation, now experimentally demonstrated, can serve to draw down atmospheric carbon dioxide. The process is cheaper and politically less intrusive than control of emissions. It also exploits excess CO_2 as a resource for enhancing ocean fisheries. [1]

Introduction

The fact that human activities are changing the chemical composition of the atmosphere has become a cause of concern for much of the public. The first question to ask, certainly, is: What are the physical consequences of this 'grand geophysical experiment' – as Professor Roger Revelle, the 'father' of greenhouse warming theory, referred to it. How significant are its effects on global climate, ecological values, and human welfare? The second question is: What, if anything, can and should be done about it?

With regard to the first question, there is the extreme, alarmist position that visualises concentrations of greenhouse gases, principally carbon dioxide (CO_2), increasing to levels that have not been experienced on the Earth since the age of the dinosaurs. The consequences, based on unverified theoretical climate models and fanciful speculations, are pictured to be catastrophic.

---

[1] This essay is based on the author's forthcoming book Global Warming: Unfinished Business.

A rather different point of view considers the facts that, in sharp contrast to the results from computer models, climate data are showing no current warming (Spencer and Christy 1992) – in spite of a rise in anthropogenic greenhouse gases equivalent to a 50% increase in CO_2; that there have been natural climate variations in the last several thousand years, which are larger and more rapid than those predicted by computer models (Keigwin 1996); that any future warming may result in a slowdown, not an acceleration, of the ongoing rise in sea level (Singer 1997); and that rising atmospheric CO_2 concentrations are a boon to agriculture (Idso 1989).

And, of course, there are opinions in between these two positions. It should be recognized, however, that there is a consistent bias in the development of our current understanding of greenhouse warming and most other environmental problems. Nearly all research is funded by government; the rationale for so expending tax-payers' money is to prevent hazards to the general welfare. But this means that essentially no research funds are provided to look for possible benefits from man's impact on the environment.

Hence benefits are not documented and quantified, due to lack of incentives in the form of available research support (Bate, 1996).

Panicky versus Prudent Measures

With regard to the second question, the activist position is to try to stabilise the atmospheric concentration of CO_2 – even if this requires a world-wide reduction in present emission levels, and in energy use, by 60 to 80%! They visualise an elaborate scheme of setting national energy budgets – which is essentially a rationing system. Energy taxes would be imposed, including a legal 'black market' that would permit the buying and selling of emission rights between nations. Even without national and international taxes, such an emission control scheme would depress GDP by several percent, imposing costs on the world economy in the multi-trillion dollar range, causing hardships for low-income groups and for the poorest nations (Manne and Richels 1991).

Since we have no scientific guidance on what constitutes a 'dangerous' level of greenhouse gases, a more reasonable position is to institute prudent measures that make sense even without the threat of global warming disasters. Such measures, many of which have already been put in place, include energy conservation and efficiency improvements. (Electric powerplants are continuing to show higher conversion efficiencies; in future, hybrid electric cars using regenerative braking, might easily achieve twice the fuel economy of the present automobile fleet.)

A complementary approach is to encourage the use of nuclear and other alternative energy sources, and mitigate any negative effects of climate change in the same way one tries to mitigate the effects of the much larger natural climate variations.

The most reasonable policy is to adapt to climate change, as human activities normally adapt to seasonal and year-to-year variations. One can then use the funds saved to strengthen the resilience of populations, particularly in developing countries, against extreme climate events that cause damage.

Sequestering Atmospheric CO_2

Many energy specialists consider the period of fossil fuel use – and elevated CO_2 levels – to be limited to one or two centuries, a mere blip on the time scale of human existence. Still, given the many uncertainties about how climate change comes about, it might make sense to speed up the natural absorption of excess atmospheric CO_2 into the biosphere and ocean.

With the residence time of atmospheric CO_2 variously estimated as between 50 and 200 years, its current excess over its pre-industrial value will eventually be absorbed by biota on land and in the ocean anyway. But if a future warming is negligibly small and on the whole beneficial, there may still be political pressure to control the level of atmospheric carbon dioxide. The standard approach, and the one most appealing to international bureaucrats, has been to control CO_2 emission rates; for example, the 1990 IPCC report pointed out that maintaining the current level of CO_2 (350 ppm) would require a world-wide emission reduction of 60 to 80% from 1990 rates – with a corresponding reduction in energy use (IPCC 1990). Stabilising at the 550 ppm level, approximately double the pre-industrial value, requires an emission reduction of some 50%. It is hard to imagine broad political support for such a plan given the disastrous economic consequences it would entail. Fully realising this, politicians have instead talked about more modest reductions of between 5 and 20% from current rates – with more to come later. But even if these reduced rates were to be achieved on a world-wide basis, they would do no more than to slow down somewhat – and at great cost – the current upward trend of atmospheric CO_2. Stabilising emissions does not stabilise concentration if the atmospheric residence time is so long that CO_2 accumulates.

120

An alternative approach to emission control is to sequester the CO_2 from the atmosphere – or at least to demonstrate that sequestering is technically and economically feasible. The conventional approach to CO_2 sequestration has called for tree planting on a massive scale, thereby tying up CO_2 for decades, to be released when the wood decays. But tree planting can be costly and impractical; it requires huge areas and great expenditures of funds to make an appreciable impact. Order-of-magnitude figures for sequestration by trees are 0.8 – 1.6 tonnes of carbon per hectare per year (Nordhaus 1991); thus, to absorb current production of about 6 gigatons CO_2 requires about 50 million km^2 (ca. 4500x4500 miles!). A relatively low-cost policy, however, would be a programme to use as much lumber as possible in all permanent structures and reseed existing forests.

Ocean Fertilisation

An equally effective, and economically attractive, scheme is to speed up the natural absorption of CO_2 into the ocean. Currently, much of the world's oceans is a biological desert. Even though many of these areas have adequate supplies of the basic nutrients, nitrates and phosphates, they lack essential micronutrients like iron. Ocean fertilisation (McElroy 1983) has been widely discussed among scientific specialists, with experiments proposed by the late John Martin (Martin 1990, 1994), and endorsed by the late Professor Roger Revelle, director of the Scripps Oceanographic Institution in La Jolla, California.

With the completion and publication of the successful IronEx-II test (see papers in the Oct. 10, 1996 issue of *Nature*), it now makes sense to consider ocean fertilisation as a viable candidate for sequestering atmospheric CO_2.

The biomass of phytoplankton in the world's oceans amounts to only one to two percent of the total global plant carbon; yet these organisms fix between 30 to 50 billion metric tonnes of carbon (Gt C) annually, which is about 40% of the total. (For reference, the atmosphere contains 750 Gt C in the form of CO_2.)

The ocean fertilisation experiments, specifically the IronEx-II test, show that, in the equatorial Pacific Ocean at least, the growth of phytoplankton can be dramatically increased by the addition of minute quantities of inorganic iron to surface water. In common with the Southern Ocean, and, to a lesser extent, parts of the Northeast Pacific, these waters are termed 'high-nutrient, low-chlorophyll' (HNLC), meaning that the normal nutrients, nitrate and phosphate, are found at the surface, but are not used by the plankton. Addition of the micronutrient iron permits uptake of these unused nutrients and an associated amount of inorganic carbon.

An uncontrolled experiment, the eruption of the volcano Pinatubo, provided an additional test and has led to estimates that can be used for planning a drawdown of atmospheric CO_2. The eruption injected crustal material, about 3% iron by weight, into the troposphere and lower stratosphere, and spread it over the globe. Smaller particles may have been carried far enough to enhance productivity in distant HNLC regions, by far the largest of which is the Southern Ocean. Using estimates of the mass deposition flux there, Andrew Watson estimates that the iron deposited amounted to roughly 40,000 tonnes (Watson 1997). (This amount is 100,000 times that used in the IronEx-II experiment.) Given a typical carbon/iron molar ratio of 10^5 for phytoplankton in iron-limited regions, this would enable additional new production, using up about 7×10^{13} mol of carbon. Such an increase would then release a pulse of the order of 10^{14} mol of oxygen into the atmosphere – which is consistent with changes in the hemispheric gradient of the O_2/N_2 ratio observed by R.F. Keeling et al. (Keeling et al 1996).

A simple calculation shows that a full-scale demonstration releasing 1 million tonnes (Mt.) of iron in HNLC regions can tie up 20 Gt C, which would then be replenished from the atmosphere over some period of time. The drawdown of atmospheric CO_2 would depend on the rate of grazing by zooplankton and higher animals, i.e., on the effectiveness of the 'biological CO_2 pump,' which rapidly transfers carbon from surface waters to the ocean bottom. (Paul Falkowski (1997) has pointed out that iron fertilisation would also increase phytoplankton growth in regions where there is insufficient nitrogen – by stimulating bacterial nitrogen fixation; he estimates that this might increase CO_2 drawdown by a factor of 3 to 4.) There was a slowdown observed in the rate of increase of atmospheric carbon dioxide following the Pinatubo eruption (Sarmiento 1993). It is likely, therefore, that the atmospheric effect of the proposed demonstration would be easily measurable by existing CO_2 monitors.

Carrying out the operation would be relatively simple. Single-hulled supertankers exist in surplus; they are not suitable for carrying oil cargoes but would be ideal for transporting ferrous sulphate, a waste product, and dispersing it – all at low cost. Special patented formulations that slow the release of the iron would raise costs somewhat but greatly increase the efficiency of the iron absorption.

A large-scale demonstration is advisable, building on the scientific success of IronEx-II. It would prove the technical and economic feasibility of lowering the atmospheric CO_2 content at a fraction of the cost now contemplated for emissions reduction. While it may never be necessary to reduce atmospheric CO_2, it will be comforting to know that we have the technical capability to do so.

In Table 1 below, I have tried to estimate the costs of reducing the concentration of atmospheric CO_2 by different methods.

Additional Benefits: CO_2 as a Resource

The current excess of atmospheric CO_2 could become an important resource, to be exploited for feeding a growing world population. Large-scale fertilisation of areas of the Pacific and the Southern Ocean for the purpose of stimulating the growth of phytoplankton would draw down atmospheric CO_2 without depressing the economies of industrialized nations or limiting the economic growth options of developing nations. With phytoplankton as the base of the oceanic food chain, any increase in that population can lead to the development of new commercial fisheries in areas currently devoid of fish. Carbon dioxide from fossil fuel burning thus becomes a natural resource for humanity rather than an imagined menace to global climate.

MITIGATION OF ATMOSPHERIC CARBON DIOXIDE

By control of emissions: **Typical cost ~ \$100-200 per ton of C emitted (a)**

By reforestation: **Typical cost ~ \$50 per ton of atmospheric CO_2 (b)
equivalent to \$25 per ton of CO_2 emitted**

By ocean fertilisation:

**Assume 10^6 tons of Fe (costing ~ \$1 billion) can
sequester 2×10^{10} tons of C into biomass and needs
to be applied yearly. Assume that only 1% of C
comes from the atmosphere, equivalent to reducing
emissions by 2%, or 4×10^8 tons. (c)**

Therefore, estimated cost ~ $\$10^9/4 \times 10^8$ ~ \$2.50 per ton of C

(a) Emission control costs are known to rise rapidly as the degree of control increases (IPCC WGIII 1996, Fig. 7.3, p. 254). Besides, at the very best, emission control will only slow down somewhat the rate of increase of concentration.

(b) Estimated costs for sequestering CO_2 vary widely, from \$7 (Sedjo and Solomon 1989) to \$42-114 (Nordhaus 1991); see discussion in IPCC WGIII 1996 (pp. 352 – 355). The cost would rise as the degree of sequestration increases. (Removal of one ton per year is equivalent to reducing emissions by about 2 tons per year.) No allowance has been made for the economic value of the lumber harvested.

(c) Comparing the costs in the table, it is clear that ocean fertilisation has by far the lowest cost – \$2.50 per ton of carbon – even if one assumes that the phytoplankton draws only 1% of carbon from the atmosphere and 99% from the oceans. In addition, sequestration by ocean fertilisation should exhibit a linear cost curve, unlike forest sequestration or emission control. No allowance is made for the economic value of the fish resources.

Table 1.

References

Bate, R., Economist's Foreword in ESEF (1996), The Global Warming Debate. European Science and Environment Forum, Cambridge.

Falkowski, P. *Nature*, in press, 1997.

Idso, S.B. Carbon Dioxide and Global Change: Earth in Transition. IBR Press, Arizona, 1989.

IPCC WGI. 'Climate Change: The IPCC Scientific Assessment.' J.T. Houghton, G.J. Jenkins and J.J. Ephraums (eds.). Cambridge University Press, Cambridge, UK, 1990.

IPCC WGII. 'Climate Change 1995: Impacts, Adaptations and Mitigation of Climate Change: Scientific-Technical Analyses.' R.T. Watson, M. C. Zinyowera, R.H. Moss and D. J. Dokken (eds.). Cambridge University Press, Cambridge, UK, 1996.

IPCC WGIII. 'Climate Change 1995: Economic and Social Dimensions of Climate Change.' J.P.

Keeling, R.F., S.C. Piper and M. Heimann. 'Global and hemispheric CO_2 sinks deduced from changes in atmospheric CO_2 concentration.' *Nature*, 381, 218-221, May 16, 1996.

Keigwin, L.D., 'The Little Ice Age and Medieval Warm period in the Sargasso Sea.' *Science*, 274, 1504 – 1508, 29 Nov. 1996.

Manne, A. S., and R.G. Richels. 'Global CO_2 Emission Reductions: The Impact of Rising Energy Costs.' *Energy Journal*, 12, 87 – 107, 1991.

Martin, J. Oceanography, 4, 52-55, 1990; *Nature*, 371, 123-129, 1994.

McElroy, M. B. *Nature*, 302, 328-329, 1983.

Nordhaus, W. D. 'The cost of slowing down climate change: A survey.' *Energy J.*, 12(1), 37-65, 1991.

Sarmiento, J.L. 'Atmospheric CO_2 Stalled.' *Nature* 365, 697-370, 1993

Singer, S. F., R. Revelle and C. Starr. 'What to do about greenhouse warming: Look before you leap.' *Cosmos*, 1, 28 – 33, 1991.

Spencer, R.W., and J. R. Christy. 'Precision and Radiosonde Validation of Satellite Gridpoint Temperature Anomalies. Part II: A Tropospheric Retrieval and Trends during 1979-90.' *J. Clim.*, 5, pp. 858 – 866, 1992.

Watson, A. 'Volcanic iron, CO_2, ocean productivity and climate.' *Nature*, 385, 587-588, 1997.

S. Fred Singer

Dr. Singer, professor (emeritus) of environmental sciences at the University of Virginia, is the founding president of the Fairfax-based Science & Environmental Policy Project. SEPP is a non-profit educational association of scientists concerned with providing a sound scientific base for environmental policies. Prof. Singer has held several academic and governmental positions, including as the first director of the US Weather Satellite Service (now part of NOAA), deputy assistant administrator for policy of the Environmental Protection Agency, and most recently, chief scientist of the US Department of Transportation. The author of many scientific articles and books, he devised the instrument used to measure stratospheric ozone from satellites and was first to point to and calculate the human-based production of atmospheric methane, an important greenhouse gas and source of stratospheric water vapour.

II

Scientific Controversies

Global Warming or Little Ice Age?

Theodor Landscheidt
Schroeter Institute for Research in Cycles of Solar Activity
Belle Côte, Nova Scotia
Canada

Summary

The dominant theory of global warming is confronted with a model based on solar variability which predicts a new Little Ice Age. Analysis of major change in the sun's orbital angular momentum discloses five-fold symmetry in the dynamics of the sun's irregular motion about the centre of mass of the solar system and a fractal set of cycles based on this symmetry. A semi-quantitative model with predictive capabilities links these cycles both to the sun's activity and to its terrestrial responses. This relationship encompasses maxima and minima in the Gleissberg cycle, periods of weak sunspot activity and global cooling, thickness of varves from Lake Saki, temperature in the Northern Hemisphere, U.S. drought, geomagnetic storms, and rainfall in Germany, England, U.S.A., and India. Most of these consistent data connections cover centuries and indicate a solution of the problem of phase reversals in solar-terrestrial cycles. The model points to a period of global cooling in the coming decades. Solar activity as well as surface temperatures are expected to reach a deep minimum around 2026.[1]

Introduction

The Intergovernmental Panel on Climatic Change (IPCC), a body of civil servants and scientists who dominate the public discussion on the greenhouse effect, predicted in 1990 and 1992 by means of general circulation models (GCM) that global temperature would reach a range of warming from 2°-5°C by 2100 because of the increasing carbon dioxide content of the atmosphere. The corresponding mean warming rate higher than ever observed in 10,000 years. The IPCC also expected a sea level rise of at least

---

[1] An earlier version of this paper appeared in the *Journal of Coastal Research*, Special Issue No. 17: Holocene Cycles: Climate, Sea Levels, and Sedimentation, 371-382.

0.65 m by 2100. This implies an unheard-of rise rate of 5.9 mm/yr. The facts are quite different. According to a consensus in the earth science community established in the decade before 1990, the current rate of mean sea level rise is 1.8 ± 0.3 mm/yr, based on analysis of long tide gauge records (Douglas, 1991). There is no evidence of acceleration in the last 100-150 years (Baltuck et al., 1996). Geological studies even indicate that the rate of sea level rise has been constant since the Middle Ages (Nydick et al., 1995). It seems very likely that any acceleration in sea level rise over the past few hundred years is from natural and not anthropogenic causes, and it may be related to the warming of earth's climate following the Little Ice Age (Baltuck et al., 1996). The IPCC prediction furthermore ignored the fact that satellite data available since 1979, the only truly global temperature measurements, did not show any warming at all, but actually a slight cooling of 0.05°C per decade. In 1995 the temperature in the low troposphere measured by orbiting satellites was just as high as in 1979 (Singer, 1996; Michaels and Knappenberger, 1996). In 1990, the consistent increase in the carbon dioxide accumulation in the atmosphere suddenly came to an end. A sharp decline has left scientists wondering what has happened (Leutwyler, 1994). It is obvious that the general circulation models, on which the IPCC predictions are based, do not reflect the actual development in the atmosphere. For a variety of reasons, in 1995 the IPCC reduced the expected range of warming by 2110 to $1^{\circ} - 3.5^{\circ}$ C and now predicts a sea level rise far below the level of the former forecast.

There has been a significant investment in the supercomputers on which the IPCC climate models were developed. Yet the models produce nothing else but trend ranges, which do not conform with reality. Actually, the global temperatures do not follow a continually ascending trend line, but form an undulating pattern, as shown by the thick line in Figure 1. The IPCC models do not even try to emulate this climate feature. Yet as early as 1991, Friis-Christensen and Lassen provided evidence that the Northern Hemisphere temperature variation is closely linked to the length of the 11-year sunspot cycle. Figure 1 shows this relationship. The length of the 11-year cycle is a measure of the intensity of solar activity. Short cycles generate high sunspot maxima, whereas long cycles are characterised by weaker sunspot activity. These variations in the amplitude of the 11-year cycle are modulated by the secular sunspot cycle of about 90 years. It immediately emerges when the lengths of consecutive 11-year cycles are smoothed (Gleissberg, 1955). Thus, the parallel course of the low pass filtered cycle length (thin line, left scale) and the temperature variation (thick line, right scale) in Figure 1 connects the global surface temperature in the Northern Hemisphere directly with the secular sunspot cycle, also called the Gleissberg cycle. Lassen and Friis-Christensen (1996) extended this connection back to 1579. Butler (1996) corroborated it by a replication covering the temperature time series for Armagh Observatory 1796 – 1992. Unlike the IPCC models, the Gleissberg cycle follows all those ups and downs in the temperature curve.

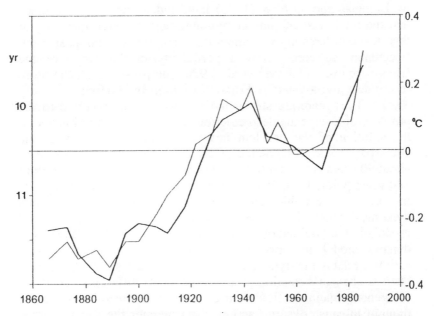

Figure 1: Association of the length of the 11-year sunspot cycle (thin line, left scale) with the Northern Hemisphere temperature (thick line, right scale). From Friis-Christensen and Lassen, 1991.

There is a physical explanation of this close correlation. Satellite instruments revealed that the sun's brightness decreased by about 0.1% between the peak of sunspot activity in 1980 and its minimum in autumn 1986, whereas the sun grew more luminous in the ascending phase of the new cycle (Willson and Hudson, 1991). This was surprising as scientists had thought that growing sunspots would impede the free flow of energy near the sun's surface and thus diminish the sun's brightness. Analysis by Foukal and Lean (1988) has yielded an explanation: the increase in bright faculae outweighs the increase in dark spots when the sun's activity is on the rise. The equilibrium response of the terrestrial

131

temperature to a 0.1% change in the sun's radiative output is at the order of 0.2º C (Hansen and Lacis, 1990). Calculations based on standard climate models show that a dip in the solar irradiance of between 0.2 and 0.5%, acting over several decades, would have been sufficient to cause the Little Ice Age (Foukal, 1990 a; Reid, 1991). Thus, it is no longer unimaginable that the Gleissberg cycle gathers sufficient potential for climatic change by steady accumulation of excess radiation or continued decrease in the radiation level over a period of nine or even more decades. Studies by Baliunas and Jastrow (1990) have indeed provided evidence that the brightness of stars comparable with our sun does vary at this level. Interestingly, temperature records of the past from Greenland ice cores show a periodicity in the range of the Gleissberg cycle (Johnsen et al., 1970) comparable with the more recent data investigated by Friis-Christensen and Lassen.

Thus there are strong indications that the solution to the problem of a dependable prediction of climate change hinges on the solution of the problem how to predict the course of the Gleissberg cycle. Knowledge of the mean length of this cycle of about 90 years is no real help in this respect as it varies from 40 to 120 years (Gleissberg, 1975). Simple mean computer deliberations indicate that variable but computable features in the sun's dynamics, which show a relationship with the sun's activity and especially the Gleissberg cycle, could offer a solution. Babcock's dynamo model, the only existing rudimentary theory of sunspot activity, relates the dynamics of the magnetic Hale cycle of 22.1 years to the sun's rotation. The interaction of differential rotation, the general magnetic field, and convection in the solar plasma is thought to cause dynamo action that generates the sunspot cycle by magnetic-field amplification. So it might be expected that variations in the sun's rotation rate are reflected in the level of sunspot activity. Accordingly, Clark et al. (1979) could show that in 1957, when the sunspot activity was nearly three times more intense than in 1884, the differential rotation in the sunspot zone took half a day longer than in 1884. Chistyakov (1976), Godoli and Mazzuconi (1979), Balthasar and Woehl (1980), and Howard (1984) confirmed this result.

Yet the sun's spin momentum, related to its rotation on its axis, is only one component of its total angular momentum. The other part, the sun's orbital angular momentum, is related to its irregular oscillation about the centre of mass of the solar system (CM). Its contribution to the total angular momentum is not negligible. It varies from -0.1×10^{47} to 4.3×10^{47} g/cm^2 s^{-1} or conversely, which is more than a forty-fold increase or decrease. The maximum value of the orbital momentum reaches 25% of the sun's spin momentum which is 1.7×10^{48} g/cm² s⁻¹.

If there were transfer of angular momentum from the sun's orbit to the spin on its axis, this could make a difference of more than 7 per cent in its equatorial rotational velocity (Blizard, 1987). Such acceleration or deceleration has been actually observed (Landscheidt, 1976). The giant planets Jupiter, Saturn, Uranus, and Neptune, that regulate the sun's motion about the centre of mass, carry more than 99% of the total angular momentum in the solar system, while the sun is confined to less than 1%. This seems to be indicative of a case of spin-orbit coupling of the spinning sun and the sun revolving about the centre of mass, involving transfer of angular momentum from the outer planets to the revolving sun and eventually to the spinning sun (Landscheidt, 1983, 1987, 1988). With respect to the angular momentum conservation law, it makes sense that the observed slowing down in the sun's spin regularly coincides with an increase in the sun's orbital angular momentum. Part of the coupling could result from the sun's motion through its own magnetic fields. The low corona acts as a brake on the sun's surface (Dicke, 1964).

So it seems reasonable to investigate the strong variation in the sun's orbital angular momentum with respect to cycles in the sun's activity and in terrestrial climate. Surprisingly, this search will yield hitherto unknown solar cycles and their connections with long range variations in the earth's climate, mean surface air temperature averaged over the Northern Hemisphere, Lake Saki varve thickness and other climatic or geophysical phenomena. Contrary to the IPCC models, these connections seem to open up new possibilities for dependable long range predictions.

Secular Variation In The Sun's Orbital Angular Momentum And Minima In The Gleissberg Cycle

Figure 2 shows the 36-year running variance (v) in the sun's orbital angular momentum (L) for A.D. 700 to 1600. The running variance technique applies the well-known smoothing procedure of running means over two, three, or more consecutive readings to variance, the square of the standard deviation. All extrema in the variance curve, minima as well as maxima, coincide with consecutive minima in the Gleissberg cycle. Arrows mark the observed epochs of these minima assessed by Gleissberg (1955) and Link (1978). The obvious correlation covering nine centuries seems to solve the problem of how to forecast periods of weak solar activity and colder climate. Yet this is not so. An extension from A.D. 1600 to 2100 exposes instabilities in the pattern. The deep Gleissberg minimum in 1810 does not coincide with the variance extremum in 1830, the variance extremum in 1925 is far away from the Gleissberg minimum in 1900, and the variance extremum around 1990 coincides with a period of strong sunspot activity, not with a secular minimum. A more detailed analysis seems to be indicated. Re-normalisation transformations involving a change of scale have proven to be a useful research tool. So we choose a finer scale that amplifies the variance curve in Figure 2.

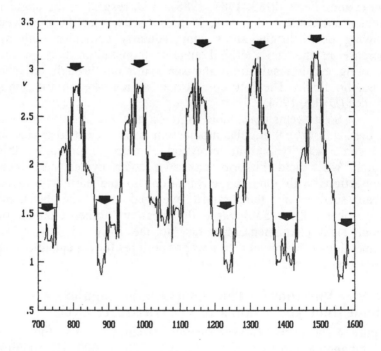

Figure 2:   Correlation between the 36-year running variance in the sun's orbital angular momentum (v) and the Gleissberg cycle of sunspot activity A.D. 700 to 1600. All extrema in the variance *v* coincide with minima in the secular sunspot cycle, the epochs of which are indicated by arrows.

134

Five-Fold Symmetry In The Sun's Dynamics

Figure 3 shows the smoothed 9-year running variance of the sun's orbital angular momentum (rv) for A.D. 720 to 1070. Amazingly, it reveals 'five-fingered hands', a clear indication of five-fold symmetry. Scientists conceive the sun as a body composed of dead matter. As such, the sun should not display five-fold symmetry. Two-fold, three-fold, four-fold, or six-fold symmetry like crystals, but not five-fold symmetry reserved for the realm of biology. Yet the existence of five-fold symmetry in the sun's dynamics is not an isolated phenomenon. It complements the discovery of five-fold symmetry in quasicrystals by Shechtman and his colleagues in 1984. The 'fingers' in Figure 3 as well as in Figures 4 and 5 are numbered for identification. I call them big fingers (BFs), because there are also small ones. A complete big hand (BH) covers a mean period of 178.8 years. This is a fundamental cycle in the sun's motion discovered by Jose (1965) in his pioneer computer analysis. Jose found this cycle also in sunspots. According to Dansgaard et al. (1973), a period of 181 years, rather close to 178.8 years, is the paramount cyclic feature of the oxygen isotope profile in the Camp Century ice core.

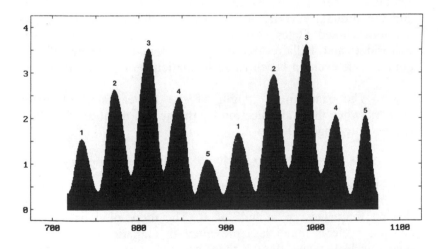

Figure 3: Smoothed 9-year running variance of the sun's orbital angular momentum *rv* A.D. 720 to 1070. This amplified view of the data in Figure 2 reveals five-fold symmetry expressed by 'hands' with five 'fingers'.

135

The mean interval covered by big fingers is 178.8 years / 5 = 35.76 years. The big finger cycle (BFC) of this length does not only show a high degree of correlation with the Gleissberg cycle, but also an exact relationship with the magnetic Hale cycle of 22.1 years and the sunspot cycle of 11.05 years. Since the establishment of the KAM theorem by Kolmogorov (1979), Arnold (1963), and Moser (1973), it is an acknowledged fact that the golden section plays an important role in the solar system dynamics. The stability of the planetary system hinges on it. The golden section is intimately connected with five-fold symmetry (Kapraff, 1991). Thus, the emergence of five-fold symmetry in the dynamics of the sun's motion about the centre of mass is another indication of the importance of the golden section for the solar system and especially the sun's activity. The golden number G = 0.618 – mathematically the most irrational of all irrational numbers represents the golden mean. When multiplied by the length of the BFC, the exact Hale period emerges:

35.76 years [BFC] × 0.618 [G] = 22.1 years [Hale cycle].

The 22-year cycle is a dominant feature in the global record of marine air temperatures, consisting of shipboard temperatures measured at night (Burroughs, 1992), the de-trended Central England temperature record for A.D. 1700 to 1950 (Mason, 1976), and the drought severity index covering different areas of the Western United States (Mitchell, Stockton, and Meko, 1979). Fairbridge and Hillaire-Marcel (1977) found evidence of the double Hale cycle in beach ridge formations going back to 8 000 BC.

The exact mean length of the 11-year sunspot cycle appears, when the multiplication by the golden number is applied to a half big finger (HBF):

17.88 years [HBF] × 0.618 [G] = 11.05 years [sunspot cycle].

It is not an arbitrary procedure to divide cycles into halves. Observation shows that spectral peaks can appear at twice the driving frequency, or at half of it. The more obvious 11-year sunspot cycle is much less prevalent in climatic data than the magnetic Hale cycle, though there are many more investigations looking for potential links between the 11-year cycle and climate. The only solid link has been established by Labitzke and van Loon (1990). It correlates solar flux with QBO phases, 700 mb height and surface temperatures.

136

Rhythmic Patterns in the Sun's Orbital Momentum and Forecast of Maxima and Minima in the Gleissberg Cycle

Figure 4 displays the smoothed 9-year *rv* for A.D. 700 to 1600. This is the same range of data as in Figure 2, but amplified by a factor of four, so that more details of the variance in the sun's orbital angular momentum become visible.

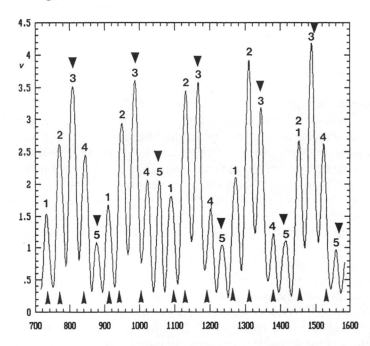

Figure 4: View of Figure 3 extended to A.D. 1600. The tips of big fingers (BFT) maxima in the 9-year running variance are numbered. BFT3s and BFT5s designate minima in the secular sunspot cycle, the epochs of which are marked by triangles. BFTs 1, 2, and 4 indicate secular maxima marked by arrows pointing upwards. Perturbation of the penta-rhythm seems to induce instability. The rightmost hand, lacking a finger, coincides with the Spoerer minimum, a period of global cooling.

Epochs of Gleissberg minima are marked by triangles pointing downwards, and epochs of Gleissberg maxima are indicated by arrows pointing upwards. It is easy to see that BF3s and BF5s coincide with Gleissberg minima, without exception, whereas BF1s, BF2s, and BF4s go along with Gleissberg maxima. The crucial phases are the maxima in *rv*, the 'finger-tips' (BFT). Consecutive BF1s and BF2s indicate periods of protracted higher sunspot activity with an intermittent lull, while BF4s point to

137

secular maxima concentrated on a single spell of secular activity. This rhythmic pattern is very sensitive to disturbances. Figure 4 shows that the rightmost hand is 'mutilated'. It lacks one finger. Instead of consecutive BF1 and BF2 and two separate periods of enhanced activity, there was only one finger and one relatively weak spell of activity around the middle of the fifteenth century. Remarkably, this phase anomaly coincided with the beginning of the Spörer minimum, a period of exceptionally weak sunspot activity and cool climate. According to Eddy (1976), it extended from 1460 to 1550. Figure 5, presenting the smoothed 9-year *rv* for A.D. 1500 to 2100, shows the effect of a different kind of disturbance that did not occur from A.D. 700 to 1600, the period covered in Figures 2 and 4. Around 1632, 1811, and 1990 the sun's motion relative to the centre of mass was retrograde and the orbital angular momentum, which had been positive for centuries, became negative. Jose (1965) was the first to point to this phenomenon. Shirley (1988) has related it to volcanic activity and climate. Retrograde phases (RP) are very rare events. The last RP before 1632 occurred in the 5th century, around 482. The next event after 1990 is to be expected around 2169. The intervals between consecutive RP range from 178 years to more than a thousand years. In Figure 5, RP events are marked by R. They are without exception linked to BF2s. The change in the sign of the orbital angular momentum in 1632 did not induce a change in the phase of the rhythmic pattern. Yet it is conspicuous that BF3, following BF2 (R), coincided with the Maunder minimum. In the unsmoothed *rv* the epoch of BFT3 falls on 1680. This is just the bottom of the Maunder minimum running from A.D. 1645 to 1715 (Schove, 1983).

RP event 1811 is linked to a phase shift. BF2 (R) should have indicated a secular sunspot maximum. Instead it coincided with the deepest Gleissberg minimum observed after the Maunder minimum. This phase reversal, the only case in 14 centuries, also affected the following BF3 and BF4. Open triangles in Figure 5 label this perturbed period; triangles pointing upwards mark the epochs of Gleissberg maxima, while those pointing downwards designate Gleissberg minima. BF5 at the beginning of the twentieth century restored the regular rhythm. The extended period of weak sunspot activity from 1880 to 1930 reflects the circumstance that BF4, irregularly connected with a Gleissberg minimum, was followed by BF5 that regularly coincides with secular minima. So far, the twentieth century has continued to follow the regular cyclic pattern. BF1 reached its peak in the second half of the 1950s when the sunspot activity was extremely strong. After an intermittent decrease around 1970, there was a steep ascent again. BF2 peaked at the end of the 1980s. This marks the epoch of a further Gleissberg maximum, which is in accord with high sunspot activity observed in 11-year cycles 21 and 22.

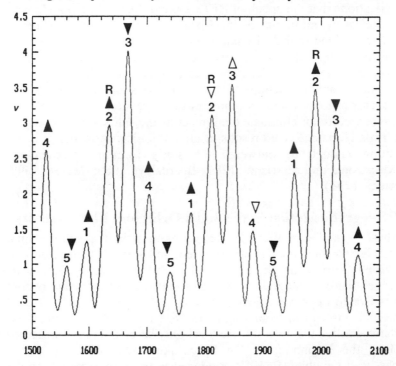

Figure 5:   Pendatactyl pattern of 9-year running variance of the sun's orbital angular momentum A.D. 1500 to 2100. Triangles pointing upwards and downwards mark epochs of maxima and minima in the 80 to 90-year Gleissberg cycle of sunspot activity. Perturbing phases of retrograde solar motion, designated by R, seem to be linked to phase instability. After the retrograde motion around 1811, the extrema in the correlated Gleissberg cycle switched phase. Open triangles focus attention on this anomaly, the only event in 1300 years of investigated data. Retrograde motion around 1632 and 1990 did not perturb the regular rhythm. BFT3 after 1632, however, coincided with the Maunder minimum. The epoch 2026 of BFT3 could have similar implications, as it follows R 1990.

It should not be forgotten, however, that BFC2 is characterised by instability, as it coincides with retrograde solar motion and negative angular momentum. Considering that change in the sun's orbital angular momentum is fundamental to our concept, it seems to be consistent to assume that a switch in sign will have an effect.

As a phase reversal like that around 1811 did not occur, the anomaly will probably affect the dimension of the secular minimum related to BF3. A comparable situation occurred around 1680 when BF3, following retrograde solar motion in 1632, concurred with the Maunder minimum. So there are substantial indications that the epoch of BFT3 around 2026 will coincide with a Gleissberg minimum of the Maunder minimum type. There is also a decided probability that the expected weak sunspot activity will go along with a long lasting decrease in irradiation and cold climate, a new Little Ice Age. The connection with solar system dynamics and the length of the data series involved gives this forecast a good chance to come close to reality. The greenhouse effect would not eliminate the impact of the sun's variation on the earth's climate. Recent results of climatologists show that it is not strong enough to outweigh the sun's forcing (Ramanathan, Barkstrom, and Harrison, 1989; Beardsley, 1989; Meier, 1990; Kiehl, 1991).

Retrograde Motion in the Sun's Orbit and Flare Activity

There is evidence that the change of sign in the sun's orbital angular momentum has actually released instability in the solar plasma. Further amplification and calculations on a finer scale reveal that the change in the sun's orbital angular momentum from positive to negative values occurred on September 1, 1989. Just around this epoch, from August to October 1989, energetic solar flares emitted the most intense level of solar cosmic rays measured since the beginning of the Space Age. One of these flares, observed October 19, 1989, produced more cosmic rays than the previous solar cycle in total (Siscoe, 1991). The count of energetic particles reached 40 000 particle flux units (pfu) with energies above 10 MeV. Had there been an astronaut on the moon, wearing only a spacesuit, death would have been probable (Joselyn, 1992). The earth's magnetic field responded with a heavy geomagnetic storm. Through 1990 there were no energetic eruptions on the sun. This changed again, when the sun's orbital angular momentum returned to positive values on January 11, 1991. A barrage of energetic events began in January 1991 and ended in June 1991. A proton flare observed on March 23, 1991 was even more spectacular than the energetic event in October 1989. It reached the flux level of 43 000 pfu (Solar-Geophysical Data, 1992). A heavy geomagnetic storm followed on March 24, 1991.

Solar Motion and Lake Saki Varve Thickness

The following results demonstrate that our semi-quantitative model does not only predict the sun's long-range variability and the related broad-scale features of the earth's global temperature, but shows a versatility and predictive capability those supercomputer models sustained by the IPCC do not even aim at. As to the Gleissberg cycle of sunspot activity, the maximum of *rv*, the (BFT), has turned out to be crucial. Yet the minimum of *rv*, the start of big fingers (BFS) also proves relevant. The thickness of Lake Saki varves is related to local precipitation: the thickest varves are linked to very wet years and the thinnest varves to very dry years (Shostakovich, 1934, 1936). The maxima in the Lake Saki varve thickness are consistently correlated with consecutive BFSs and BFTs (Landscheidt, 1990). This analysis covers the varve data from A.D. 700 to 1894. A Monte Carlo model and Student's *t*-test yielded $t = 8.2$ for 33 degrees of freedom. The null hypothesis of no connection between the studied epochs can be rejected at a high level of significance ($P < 6 \times 10^{-7}$).

Solar Angular Momentum and Northern Hemisphere Temperature

Figure 6 from Jones (1988) points at a relationship between BFSs and temperature. It shows the time series 1850 to 1987 of the annual-mean surface air temperature averaged over the Northern Hemisphere, expressed as departures in °C from the reference period 1951 to 1970. The arrows designate the BFS epochs that fall in the data range. The BFSs of 1866, 1900, and 1933 mark the outstanding temperature maxima relative to the environment, as indicated by the smoothed curve. The BFS of 1968, however, indicates the bottom of a downtrend that began after the BFS of 1933. Obviously, this is due to a phase reversal in the BFS pattern. Contrary to purely statistical investigations, the semi-quantitative model presented here can give an explanation. We have learnt from experimentation with electrical and mechanical control equipment that at nodal points, where the response of the system is zero, the phase can shift by π radians. The start of a big finger is such a nodal point. Yet it is crucial that the BFS of 1933 is at the same time the start of a big hand (BHS) which extends to the year 2111. Such nodal points higher up in the hierarchy of cycles in the sun's dynamics are dominant. According to my experience, they often induce phase reversals or other forms of cyclic instability in subordinate cycles. If the new rhythm holds, the epoch of the

coming BFS in 2007 should go along with another bottom in the
global temperature.

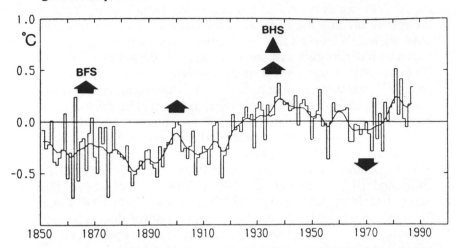

Figure 6:   Annual means of surface air temperature averaged over the Northern
Hemisphere, from Jones, 1988. The epochs of big finger starts (BFS) are marked by
arrows. Up to the start of a big hand (BHS) around 1933, marked by an open triangle,
BFSs coincided with secular maxima relative to the environment, set off by the smoothed
curve. After a phase reversal, linked to the BHS of 1933, the BFS of 1968 coincided with a
secular minimum of temperature. If the reversed rhythmic pattern holds, the BFS around
2007 should go along with another bottom in the surface air temperature.

The Sun's Orbital Momentum and U.S. Drought

U.S. drought data show a similar relationship. Figure 7 shows the
Palmer Drought Index for the U.S. from 1900 to 1989. The
vertical axis measures the percentage of area covered by drought.

The arrows mark consecutive epochs of BFSs and BFTs.
Up to 1933, the starts of big fingers (S) coincided with drought
maxima and the tips (T) with minima. After the BHS of 1933,
indicated by an open triangle, the correlation with BF phases
continued, but a phase reversal changed the rhythmic pattern. Now
BFTs coincided with drought peaks and BFSs with minima. The
new rhythm has been stable since 1933. So there is a good chance
that it will continue until the next BHS in 2111. For some years
around the next BFS epoch 2007 farmers in the U.S.A. should
expect wet climate. I want to mention in passing, that the deep
minimum between the BFS of 1933 and the BFT of 1955 just falls
on the golden section of this interval, indicated by a full circle and
G. This is not a fortuitous fit. I have shown (Landscheidt, 1995)
that the golden section is not only an important factor of the KAM
theorem, but also a common feature of cycles in nature.

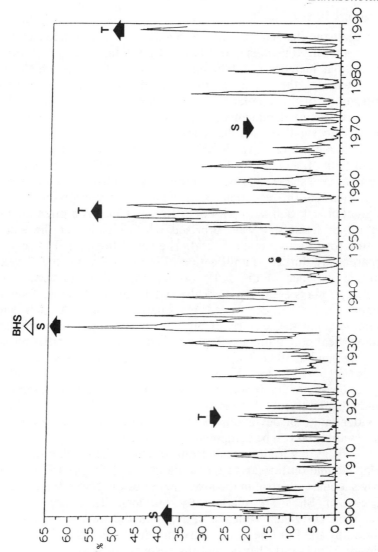

Figure 7: Association of Palmer Drought Index for the U.S., measuring the percentage of area covered by drought, with epochs of BFSs and BFTs, marked by arrows and indicators for start (S) and tip (T). The rhythmic pattern is consistent, though subjected to a phase reversal linked to the BHS of 1933, denoted by an open triangle. Up to 1933 BFSs coincided with drought peaks and BFTs with troughs. After the BHS epoch of 1933, a nodal phase of rhythmic instability, the pattern showed a reversal; BFTs went along with drought peaks and BFSs with humid periods. G and a full circle mark the golden section between the BFSs of 1933 and 1955. Remarkably, the most severe drought occurred at the start epoch of a big hand (BHS). Around 2007, the next BFS epoch, farmers in the U.S.A. should expect wet weather.

Fractals in the Sun's Dynamics

The realistic character of the aggregate of cycles related to big hands and big fingers is corroborated by the fact that they form a fractal that includes small fingers within small hands which are subjected to the same hierarchical features as the larger realisations of this similarity pattern. Phase reversals induced by nodal phases of dominant cycles can also be observed in cycles attached to small fingers that change phase after the nodal point (BFS) of a big finger. An ubiquitous notion in present-day science is the term 'fractal' coined by Mandelbrot (1983). A fractal is a geometrical shape whose complex structure is such that magnification or reduction by a given factor reproduces the original object. Self-similarity on different scales is a pre-eminent feature of fractals. I was surprised when I saw that the sun's motion forms a dynamical fractal. The small fingers (SF) become apparent by further amplification. Figure 8 shows the 3-year running variance of the sun's orbital angular momentum. The circled numbers at the top mark the epochs of BFTs. Tips of small fingers (SFT) are designated by small numbers. Arrows and triangles point to the starts of big and small fingers respectively. The vertical dotted line marks the already mentioned initial phase of a big hand in 1933. The theoretical mean width of a SF is 178.8 years / 5 / 5 = 7.2 years. Yet small hands and small fingers show a higher degree of 'morphological' anomalies. There are sometimes hands that have only three or four fingers. Accordingly, SFs show a wider range of deviations from the mean width. However, all these variations can be computed and predicted.

Figure 9 from Foukal (1990 b) relates the number of south polar faculae on the sun to the starts of small fingers (SFSs) and shows a phase reversal in the lower realm of the finger fractal. The epochs of SFSs are marked by pointers. They are without exception correlated with the extrema in the number of faculae plotted by the full line. As to maxima, the fit is rather close. The minima consistently lag behind the respective SFSs. The 22-year Hale cycle (dashed line) shows no such synchronism. A phase reversal occurred close to the BHS of 1968 marked by a triangle on the right of the plot. At the SF epoch of 1967.8 an irregular maximum emerged instead of the regular minimum that would have continued the previous phase order. The following SFS 1974.5, connected with a minimum in faculae, confirmed the new rhythmic pattern.

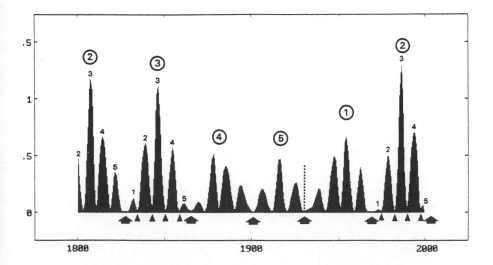

Figure 8: Plot of the 3-year running variance in the sun's orbital angular momentum. It reveals a fractal pattern: small hands with small fingers (SF) within big fingers. The epochs of BFTs are indicated by big circled numbers. SFTs are designated by small numbers. BFSs are marked by arrows and SFSs by triangles. The vertical dotted line designates the initial phase of a BH cycle of 178.8 years. The very small hand before this BHS is 'mutilated'; it has only three fingers.

The Sun's Motion, Geomagnetic Storms, And Climatic Change

Work by Wollin and colleagues at the Lamont-Doherty Geological Observatory, New York, suggests that there is a close link between changes in the earth's magnetic field and shifts in the climate around the world (Burroughs, 1992). Wilcox (1975) holds that one of the few common threads that appear so widely in the otherwise disparate literature as to suggest that they have some validity, is the link between geomagnetic storms and meteorological or geophysical responses. So it is of practical import that SFSs show a close relationship with the long-term variation in the earth's magnetic field.

Figure 10 from Solar-Geophysical Data (1994) shows the monthly mean of Mayaud's aa index of geomagnetic activity for the years 1950 to 1993. Peaks in the data point to periods characterised by strong geomagnetic storms. The triangles mark the consecutive epochs of SFSs. The correlation between crests in the curve and SFS epochs is obvious. It stands out even better in a plot of smoothed values. There is only one exception to the fit: the

145

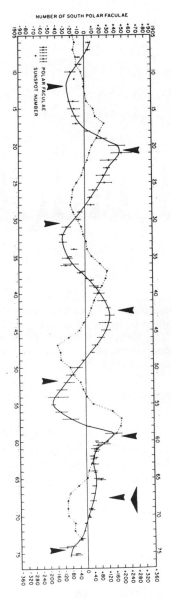

Figure 9: The solid line plots the number of south polar faculae on the sun. The extrema in the curve show a close association with SFSs, the epochs of which are marked by arrows. The 22-year magnetic solar cycle (dashed line) shows no synchronism of this kind. The start epoch of a big finger, denoted by a triangle on the right, induced a reversal in the phase of small fingers and in the sequence of extrema in the number of faculae. This is a regular feature in the hierarchy of finger cycles; it opens up a possibility to forecast phase reversal in solar-terrestrial time series. From Foukal, 1990.

146

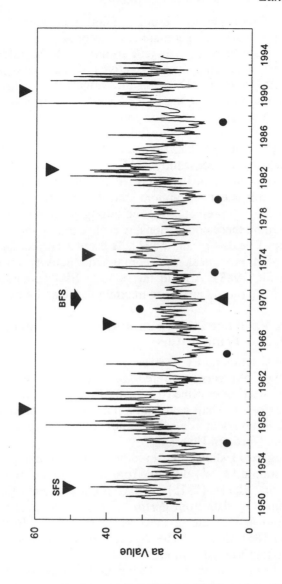

Figure 10: The curve from Solar-Geophysical Data, 1994 shows the monthly mean of Mayaud's aa-index of geomagnetic activity. The maxima in the time series, indicative of an accumulation of strong geomagnetic storms, are closely connected with the epochs of SFSs, marked by triangles. The BFS of 1968 is linked to a perturbation, the 'geomagnetic jerk' observed at this time, but induced only a temporary phase reversal. The maxima around the SFSs of 1982.8 and 1990.3 were accurately forecast on the basis of the pattern presented here. The next maxima of geomagnetic activity are to be expected around the SFS of 1998.6 and 2007.2.

147

SFS of 1970 indicated by a triangle pointing upwards. It coincides with a minimum in geomagnetic activity, described in the literature as the 'geomagnetic jerk around 1968', a sudden change in the slope of the first time derivatives of the geomagnetic field components (Courtillot, Ducruix, and Mouël, 1978). This anomaly happened at a time when the BFS of 1968 concurred with the SFS of 1970. Yet there was no permanent phase reversal. The following SFSs were again linked to peaks in geomagnetic activity. The filled circles indicate the position of the golden section in between consecutive SFSs. It regularly coincides with outstanding minima in the curve of magnetic activity. There is only one consistent exception: the temporary phase reversal around 1970. My prediction of the strong geomagnetic storms in 1982, based on these connections, was checked by the astronomers Gleissberg, Pfleiderer, and Woehl. It proved correct as well as a forecast of a new peak of geomagnetic activity around 1990 (Landscheidt, 1988). Around the coming SFS epochs of 1998.6 and 2007.2 we should again see maxima in the aa index.

Running Variance in the Sun's Angular Momentum, Rainfall, and Temperature

Rainfall and temperature likewise show a close relationship with SFSs. Lake Saki varves offered the opportunity to look into a special connection confined to local climate, but covering many centuries. Now we shall deal with a link between finger cycles and climate that covers merely 13 decades, but encompasses different areas of the Northern Hemisphere.

Figure 11 shows the smoothed 2-year running variance *vr* of yearly rainfall totals derived from observations of 14 German stations by Baur (1975). This homogeneous time series supplemented by data from *Berliner Wetterkarte*, published by the Meteorological Institute of the Free University of Berlin, covers the period 1851 to 1983. The 2-year running variance, smoothed by a Gaussian low-pass filter, focuses attention on the change in variance from year to year. Peaks in the plot point to strong contrast in the rainfall of consecutive years – very wet years follow very dry years, or very dry years follow very wet years – whereas minima indicate little contrast in this respect. Open arrows in Figure 11 mark epochs of SFSs, while open circles indicate epochs of tips of small fingers (SFTs). In terms of physics these epochs relate to minima and maxima in the 3-year running variance of the sun's orbital angular momentum. Obviously, the SFSs are regularly connected with maxima and the SFTs with

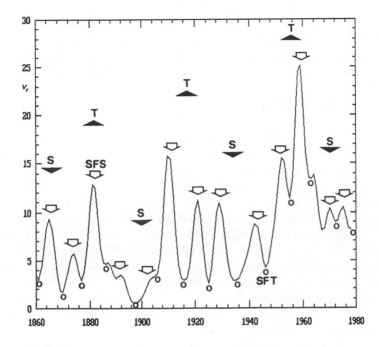

Figure 11: Smoothed 2-year running variance *vr* of yearly rainfall totals derived from observations of 14 German stations. Open arrows mark epochs of SFSs, significantly correlated with maxima in the variance, while open circles indicate epochs of SFTs that go along with minima. Only around the secular sunspot minimum 1900 the correlation is weak because of the lack of releasable magnetic energy in large sunspot groups. Variance amplitudes are modulated by starts (S) and tips(T) of BFs, marked by flat triangles. BFTs show a correlation with high amplitudes and BFSs with small ones. The SFSs of 1998.6 and 2013.6 should go along with variance amplitudes of medium height, whereas the BFS epoch 2007 will probably be related to weak variance in rainfall. This pattern, based on German data, is corroborated by rainfall observations from England, Wales, Eastern U.S.A., and India.

minima in the variance of the rainfall totals. Only around the secular sunspot minimum of 1900 the correlation is weak or even disappears. This seems to be due to the lack of releasable magnetic energy stored in large sunspot groups. The mean interval between SFSs and SFTs is 3.7 years.

The first impression of a good fit is confirmed by a series of statistical tests. The probabilities resulting from different approaches in *t*-tests range from $P < 0.0002$ to $P < 0.00003$. The null hypothesis of no correlation may be considered disproved. A replication was made with yearly rainfall averages from England

and Wales covering the years 1850 to 1976 (Lamb, 1977). The probability of false rejection of the null hypothesis of no correlation is low again: $P < 0.004$. Another replication makes use of the yearly total rainfall in the Eastern U.S., reduced to Philadelphia equivalent values for the period 1850 to 1967 (Lamb, 1977). The outcome of a test of significance is $P < 0.009$. Data from the equatorial region were also examined. Yearly monsoon season (June - September) rainfall at Bombay from 1850 to 1960 (Lamb, 1977) showed a significant correlation when a phase shift by $\pi/2$ radians was allowed for. This phase shift, emerging in low latitudes, is no ephemeral feature. It was confirmed by the analysis of All-India summer monsoon rainfall from 1871-1978 (Mooley and Parthasarathy, 1984): $P < 0.005$. Therefore, a two-phase system with relation to the geographical latitude seems to be a promising approach. Temperature opens up a further field for replication. Baur (1975) established a time series of yearly temperature averages based on the respective means of the stations Utrecht – de Bilt, Potsdam, Basle, and Vienna. With extensions taken from the *Berliner Wetterkarte*, the series covers the period 1851-1983. The highly significant result of a *t*-test is $P < 0.002$ (Landscheidt, 1988).

The maxima and minima in the variance of rainfall data in Figure 11, which show a close phase correlation with the epochs of SFSs and SFTs, are also subject to amplitude modulation linked to the change in the sun's orbital angular momentum. All periods with higher maxima concentrate on the epochs of BFTs, whereas maxima that are weak relative to the environment form clusters around epochs of BFSs. The respective epochs are marked in Figure 11 by flat triangles and an S for start and a T for tip. The SFS of 1998.6 will not be close to BF epochs. Therefore, it should go along with a maximum in the rainfall variance that reaches medium height. This forecast is restricted to the time series on which it is based. Experience shows that all time series of special data are individuals that show different patterns which reflect their complex connection with other terrestrial data and their specific relationship with variance in the sun's angular momentum. The supercomputer models promoted by the IPCC are far from showing such adaptability to individual traits of climate features.

Conclusions

The semi-quantitative model based on a fractal system of interlaced cycles linked to variance in the sun's orbital angular momentum does not present quantified mechanisms that convey a detailed cause and effect picture. It is difficult to see how it could. It tries to connect solar activity with climatic change on earth, and neither of these fields rests on a solid theoretical foundation. An accepted full theory of solar activity does not yet exist. What we have is only a hope of a future theory. According to Foukal (1990 a), 'the mechanism that causes the solar magnetic cycle remains poorly understood, although it has been the focus of intense research during the past half century.' There is a lot of literature about $\alpha\omega$-dynamos, but this is having to cope with incompatibilities of observation with theory, and does offer any explanation of longer cycles like the Gleissberg cycle that modulate the amplitudes of the 11-year cycle. The understanding of climatic change, too, is in a rudimentary stage. Especially complex coupling processes involving atmosphere, oceans and cryosphere are far from being well understood. Yet as Roederer (1993) put it, the lack of detailed insight into prevailing mechanisms is not a valid scientific argument, as most studies in natural sciences begin without any knowledge of the responsible mechanisms at all. If the fields of solar activity and climatic change shape well and develop into full-fledged theories, it is conceivable that the semi-quantitative model presented here will be better understood in detail in the new theoretical environment. It could then contribute to an interdisciplinary explanation of solar-terrestrial interaction and the development of a global predictive capability, which is the declared aim of the Solar-Terrestrial Energy Program (STEP). Successful predictions, based on change in the sun's orbital angular momentum, seem to indicate that there is substance in this expectation. In addition to the correct forecasts mentioned in this paper, I predicted the end of the Sahelian drought three years in advance (Landscheidt, 1983), and my long-range forecasts of energetic X-ray flares and strong geomagnetic storms, covering the years 1979 to 1985, reached an overall hit rate of 90 per cent (Landscheidt, 1986) though these events show a very irregular distribution. The forecasts were checked by the astronomers Gleissberg, Woehl, and Pfleiderer, as well as by the Space Environment Services Centre, Boulder, Colorado, USA. Thus, the new predictions in this paper, including the forecast of a new Little Ice Age, should prove rather reliable.

Even in the present stage of theoretical development, it seems difficult to explain the wealth of close correlations presented here as a mere coincidence, especially as the presented examples were selected from a wealth of published connections. It is a fact that most of the solar-terrestrial relationships discovered in the 1870s and the following decades vanished when examined more critically, or faded in the light of longer records. It is also true that such ephemeral relationships were limited to special regions and did not cover larger areas subjected to the same or a similar climate. Yet this kind of criticism does not apply to the results presented here that cover 1,400 years of sunspot activity, more than 130 years of temperature and rainfall in the Northern Hemisphere, and 12 centuries of Lake Saki varve data. A non-linear model of the atmosphere, developed by James and James (1989), demonstrates that large-scale features of the atmosphere, like circulation, exhibit natural internal periodicities. The strongest period emerges around 12 years, close to the 11-year sunspot cycle. Burroughs (1992) holds that this places an even greater burden of physical proof on investigations that try to link observed fluctuations in the weather to external causes like solar variability. This is a point that must be taken seriously. Yet the finger cycles investigated here have periods far from the strong 12-year periodicity, and they are coherent with quasi-periodic input that is based on solar system dynamics. The length of the finger cycles varies considerably, and the correlations closely follow these variations. This is a conspicuous feature of connections with small finger cycles that vary between 2 and 13 years. It must be a rather queer kind of coincidence that has such adaptive faculty. Moreover, the model explains for the first time why there are phase reversals in climatic time series and when they may be expected to occur. One result is quite clear: if the sun's variable activity is taken seriously as a main factor in climate change as the discovered variation in the sun's energy output and the data connection between global temperature and Gleissberg cycle require, the resulting model, developed without any public funding, is superior in every respect to the heavily-subsidised IPCC models which do not even conform with the past climatic development.

References

Arnold, W. I., 1963. Small denominators and problems of stability of motion in classical and celestial mechanics. *Russ. Math. Surv.*, 18, 85.

Baliunas, S., and Jastrow, R., 1990. Evidence for long-term brightness changes of solar-type stars. *Nature*, 348, 520.

Balthasar, H., and Woehl, H., 1980. Differential rotation and meridional motions of sunspots in the years 1940-1968. *Astron. Astrophys.*, 92, 111-116.

Baltuck, M., Dickey, J., Dixon, T., And Harrison, C. G. A., 1996. *New approaches raise questions about future sea level change.*

Baur, F., 1975. Abweichungen der Monatsmittel der Temperatur Mitteleuropas und des Niederschlags in Deutschland. *Beilage zur Berliner Wetterkarte des Instituts für Meteorologie der Freien Universität Berlin* vom 24. 6.

Beardsley, T., 1989. Not so hot: new studies question estimates of global warming. *Scientific American*, 265, 17.

Blizard, J. B., 1987. Long-range prediction of solar activity. 415-420. In: Rampino, M. R., Sanders, J. E., Newman, W. S., and Königsson, L. K., eds. *Climate: History, Periodicity, and Predictability.* New York: Van Nostrand Reinhold, 415-420.

Burroughs, W. J., 1992. *Weather Cycles Real or Imaginary.* Cambridge: Cambridge University Press.

Butler, C. J., 1996. A two-century comparison of sunspot cycle length and temperature change – the evidence from Northern Ireland. In: ESEF *The Global Warming Debate.* London: European Science and Environment Forum, Cambridge, 215-223.

Chistyakov, V. F., 1976. The rapid oscillations of the solar rotation. *Bull. Astron. Inst. Czechoslovakia*, 27, 84-91.

Clark, D. H., Yallop, B. D., Richard, S., and Emerson, B., 1979. Differential solar rotation depends on solar activity. *Nature*, 280, 299-300.

Courtillot, V. J., Ducruix, J., and Le Mouël, 1978. Sur une accélération récente de la variation séculaire du champ magnetique terrestre. *C. R. Hebd. Seances Acad. Sci.* Ser. D, 287, 1095-1098.

Damon, P. E., 1983. Solar induced variations of energetic particles at one AU. In: Schove, D. J., *Sunspot Cycles*. Stroudsburg: Hutchinson Ross, 439.

Dansgaard, W., Johnsen, S. J., Clausen, H. B., and Langway, C. C., 1973. Climatic record revealed by the Camp Century ice core. In: Turekian, K. K., ed. *The Late Cenozoic Ice Ages*. New Haven: Yale University Press, 43-44.

Dicke, R. H., 1964. The sun's rotation and relativity. *Nature*, 202, 432-435.

Douglas, B. C., 1991. Global sea level rise. *J. Geophys. Res.*, 96, 6981.

Eddy, J. A., 1976. The Maunder minimum. *Science*, 192, 1189-1202.

Fairbridge, R. W., and Hillaire-Marcel, C. 1977. An 8000-year paleoclimatic record of the 'Double-Hale' 45-year solar cycle. *Nature*, 268, 413-416.

Foukal, P., 1990 a. The variable sun. *Scientific American*, 270(2), 34-41.

Foukal, P., 1990 b. *Solar Astrophysics*. New York: John Wiley & Sons, 381.

Friis-Christensen, E., and Lassen, K., 1991. Length of the solar cycle: an indicator of solar activity closely associated with climate. *Science*, 254, 698-700.

Foukal, P., and Lean, J., 1988. An empirical model of total solar irradiance variation between 1874 and 1988. *Science*, 247, 505.

Gleissberg, W., 1955. The 80-year sunspot cycle. *British Astron. Assoc. Jour.*, 68, 148-152.

Gleissberg, W. 1975. Gibt es in der Sonnenfleckentätigkeit eine 179-jährige Wiederholungstendenz? *Veröffentlichungen des Astronomischen Institus der Universität Frankfurt*, No. 57.

Godoli, G., and Mazzuconi, F., 1979. On the rotation rates of sunspot groups. *Solar Physics*, 64, 247-254.

Hansen, J. E., and Lacis, A. A., 1990. Sun and dust versus greenhouse gases: an assessment of their relative roles in global climatic change. *Nature*, 346, 713.

Howard, R., 1984. Solar rotation. *Ann. Rev. Astron. Astrophys.*, 22, 131-155.

James, I. N., and James, P. M., 1989. Ultra-low-frequency variability in a simple atmospheric circulation model. *Nature*, 342, 54.

Johnsen, S. J., Dansgaard, W., Clausen, H. B., and Langway, C. C., 1970. Climatic oscillations 1200-2000 A.D. *Nature*, 227, 482.

Jones, P. D., 1988. Hemispheric surface air temperature variations: recent trends and an update to 1987. *J. Climate*, 1, 645-660.

Jose, P. D., 1965. Sun's motion and sunspots. *Astronomical Journal*, 70, 193-200.

Joselyn, J. A., 1992. The impact of solar flares and magnetic storms on humans. *EOS*, 73 (Feb. 18), 81.

Kappraff, J., 1991. *Connections: the Geometric Bridge Between Art and Science*. New York: McGraw-Hill.

Kiehl, J. T., 1991. Clouds and climatic change. *EOS*, 72 (March 5), 112.

Kolmogorov, A. N., 1979. Preservation of conditionally periodic movements with small change in the Hamiltonian function. *Lecture Notes in Phys.*, 93, 51.

Labitzke, K., and van Loon, H., 1990. Associations between the 11-year solar cycle, the quasi-biennial oscillation, and the atmosphere: a summary of recent work. *Phil. Trans. R. Soc. London*, A, 330, 577.

Lamb, H. H., 1977. *Climate Present, Past, and Future*, Vol. 2. London: Methuen.

Lambeck, K., 1980. *The Earth's Variable Rotation*. Cambridge: Cambridge University Press, 4.

Landscheidt, T., 1976. Beziehungen zwischen der Sonnenaktivität und dem Massenzentrum des Sonnensystems. *Nachrichten der Olbers-Gesellschaft Bremen*, 100, 3-19.

Landscheidt, T., 1983. Solar oscillations, sunspot cycles, and climatic change. In: McCormac, B. M., ed. W*eather and Climate Responses to Solar Variations*. Boulder: Colorado Associated University Press, 293-308.

Landscheidt, T. 1986. Long-range forecast of energetic X-ray bursts based on cycles of flares. In: Simon, P. A., Heckman, G., and Shea, M. A., eds. *Solar-Terrestrial Predictions*. Boulder: National Oceanic and Atmospheric Administration, 81-89.

Landscheidt, T., 1987. Long-range forecasts of solar cycles and climatic change. In: Rampino, M. R., Sanders, J. E., Newman, W. S., and Königsson, L. K., eds. *Climate: History, Periodicity, and Predictability*. New York: Van Nostrand Reinhold, 421-445.

Landscheidt, T., 1988. Solar rotation, impulses of the torque in the sun's motion, and climatic variation. *Climatic Change*, 12, 265-295.

Landscheidt, T., 1990. Relationship between rainfall in the Northern Hemisphere and impulses of the torque in the sun's motion. In: Schatten, K. H., and Arking, A., eds. *Climate Impact of Solar Variability*. NASA Conference Publication 3086, 259-266.

Landscheidt, T., 1995. Die kosmische Funktion des Goldenen Schnitts. In: Richter, P. H., ed. Sterne, Mond und Kometen. Bremen: Verlag H. M. Hauschild, 240-276.

Lassen, K. and Friis-Christensen, E., 1996. A long-term comparison of sunspot cycle length and temperature change from Zürich Observatory. In: ESEF *The Global Warming Debate*. London: European Science and Environment Forum, Cambridge, 224-232.

Leutwyler, K., 1994. No global warming? *Scientific American*, 270(2), 24.

Link, F., 1978. Solar cycles between 1540 and 1700. *Solar Physics*, 59, 175-178.

Mandelbrot, B. B., 1983. *The Fractal Geometry of Nature*. New York: Freeman.

Mason, B. I., 1976. Towards the understanding and prediction of climatic variations. *Quarterly Journal of the Royal Meteorological Society*, 102, 478.

Meier, M., 1990. Reduced rise in sea level. *Nature*, 343, 115.

Michaels, P. J. and Knappenberger, P. C., 1996. The United Nations Intergovernmental Panel on Climate Change and the scientific 'consensus' on global warming. In: ESEF *The Global*

Warming Debate. London: European Science and Environment Forum, Cambridge, 158-178.

Mitchell, J. M., Stockton, C. W., and Meko, D. M., 1979. Evidence of a 22-year rhythm of drought in the Western United States related to the Hale solar cycle since the 17th century. In: McCormac, B. M., and Seliga, T. A., eds. *Solar-Terrestrial Influences on Weather and Climate*. Dordrecht: D. Reidel, 125-143.

Mooley, D. A., and Parthasarathy, B., 1984. Fluctuations in All-India summer monsoon rainfall during 1871-1978. *Climatic Change*, 6, 287-301.

Moser, J., 1973. *Stable and Random Motions in Dynamical Systems*. Princeton: Princeton University Press.

Nydick, K. R., Bidwell, A. B., Thomas, E., and Varekamp, J. C., 1995. A sea-level rise curve from Guilford, Connecticut, U.S.A.. *Mar. Geol.*, 124, 137.

Ramanathan, V., Barkstrom, B. R., and Harrison, E. F., 1989. Climate and the earth's radiation budget. *Physics Today* (May 1989): 22-23.

Reid, G. C., 1991. Solar total irradiance variations and the global sea surface temperature record. *J. Geophys. Res.*, 96, 2835.

Roederer, J. G., 1993. STEP and global change. *STEP International*, 3(4), 4.

Shirley, J. H., 1988. When the sun goes backward: solar motion, volcanic activity, and climate, 1990-2000. In: Horovitz, J. H., ed. *Cycle Linkage: Planetary-Solar-Terrestrial*. Irvine: Foundation for the Study of Cycles, 85-92.

Shostakovich, W. B., 1934. Bodenablagerungen der Seen und periodische Schwankungen der *Natur*erscheinungen. *Memoires de l'Institut Hydrologique*, 13, 95-140.

Shostakovich, W. B., 1936. Geschichtete Bodenablagerungen der Seen als Klima. *Ann. Meteor. Zeitschr.*, 53, 176-182.

Singer, S. F., 1996. A preliminary critique of IPCC's second assessment of climate change. In: Emsley, J., ed. *The Global Warming Debate*. London: European Science and Environment Forum, 146-157

Siscoe, G. L., 1991. Solar activity. *EOS*, 72 (March 5), 113.

Solar-Geophysical Data, 1992. Solar proton events affecting the earth environment. Comprehensive reports, number 577, September 1992, 71-74.

Solar-Geophysical Data, 1994. Prompt reports, number 594, 123.

Wilcox, J. M., 1975. Solar activity and the weather. *J. Atmospher. Terr. Phys.*, 37, 237-256.

Willson, R. C., and Hudson, H. S., 1991. The sun's luminosity over a complete solar cycle. *Nature*, 351, 42.

Theodor Landscheidt

Dr Landscheidt graduated from Göttingen University in 1955. He is director of the Schroeter Institute for Research in Cycles of Solar Activity, and is on the board of directors of the International Committee for Research in Environmental Factors of the Free University of Brussels. He has published many papers on solar-climatic relationships and is engaged in the prediction of solar activity and its terrestrial responses.

Relative Impacts of Solar Irradiance Variations and Greenhouse Changes on Climate, 1880-1993

E. S. Posmentier
Long Island University, Brooklyn, NY, USA

W. H. Soon
Harvard-Smithsonian Center for Astrophysics, Cambridge, MA, USA
Mount Wilson Observatory, Mount Wilson, CA, USA

S. L. Baliunas
Harvard-Smithsonian Center for Astrophysics, Cambridge, MA, USA
Mount Wilson Observatory, Mount Wilson, CA, USA
Tennessee State University, Nashville, TN, USA

Summary

The relative roles of greenhouse gas changes and solar brightness variations in climate variability during the interval 1880-1993 are evaluated using a combination of theoretical and empirical techniques. We use an ocean-atmosphere model with time-varying greenhouse gas concentrations and time-varying solar brightness. In five simulations, either one or both of the two time-varying forcing functions is scaled to obtain optimum fit with observed global, annual average temperature variations. The optimum simulation using a combination of both forcing functions, explains 92% of the variance of observed temperature variance, and 0.64°C of the observed 0.70°C temperature range, with the solar forcing playing a somewhat larger role. The simulations imply a climate sensitivity to a doubling of carbon dioxide (CO_2) of 1.26°C.

These results are confirmed by a multiple regression analysis between observed temperatures, and variations of solar brightness and CO_2. The multiple-correlation coefficient squared (R^2) is 89.3%. The sum of the 0.33°C linear effect of greenhouse gasses, and the 0.44°C effect of solar variations, is 0.77°C, in excellent agreement with the observed temperature range of

0.70°C during the interval 1880-1993. The climate sensitivity to a doubling of CO_2 extrapolated from the statistical analysis, is 1.33°C.

1. Introduction

Numerous investigations have linked climate change on time scales of decades to centuries to variations in the Earth's greenhouse effect associated with changing levels of atmospheric CO_2 and other greenhouse gasses (*e.g.*, Tett et al., 1996).

On the other hand, Reid (1987, 1991) found that solar irradiance variations with a range of about 0.6% could explain most of the observed long-term trends in sea surface temperature since 1850. Kelly and Wigley (1992) and Schlesinger and Ramankutty (1992), using two similar bulk energy-balance models, examined the relative contributions of greenhouse gases, sulphate aerosols, and solar climate forcing. Both studies showed that the explained variance in global temperature is improved when solar forcing is combined with the radiative forcing of anthropogenic greenhouse gas emission.

Empirical relationships between solar activity and terrestrial temperature have been found, which can be explained in terms of postulated changes in the solar total irradiance (*e.g.*, Friis-Christensen and Lassen 1991; Hoyt and Schatten 1993; Hameed and Gong 1994). Additional mechanisms that may induce long-term climate changes are the modulation of tropospheric radiative properties induced by solar UV variability (Haigh 1994; Schatten 1996) or the modification of the global electric circuit and cloud microphysics caused by solar energetic particles (Tinsley, Hoeksema and Baker 1994).

It is the purpose of this paper to re-examine the relative roles of greenhouse gas changes and solar brightness variations as climate influences over the interval 1880-1993, using a combination of theoretical and empirical techniques. It is assumed throughout that Hoyt and Schatten's (1993) composite based on five indicators is the best proxy for solar brightness variations (Soon, Posmentier, and Baliunas 1996, referred to below as SPB96)

2. Modelling

The first of two approaches we use to evaluate the relative roles of solar and greenhouse forcing in climate variability is a modelling approach. We use a climate model with time-varying greenhouse gas (GHG) concentrations and time-varying solar brightness, and scale either one or both of these two forcing functions with 'stretching factors' *a* and *b*, to obtain optimum fit with observed annual global land air surface temperature from 1880-1993 compiled by Hansen and Lebedeff (1987, 1988).

2.1 DESCRIPTION OF THE CLIMATE MODEL

The energy conservation climate model used in this study is an extension of the Posmentier (1994) model used by SPB96. It resolves seven zones – three in each hemisphere and one intertropical convergence zone. Each zone is divided into land and ocean areas, with one and two layers, respectively. The model atmosphere consists of two layers in each of the fourteen regions. The physical processes accounted for by the model include: radiation in three wavelength bands; parameterized evaporation, precipitation and cloudiness; advection and diffusion in three dimensions; and surface sensible heat exchange. The model equations are integrated using 256 time steps per year. Further details of the model, and validation data, are discussed by SPB96.

2.2 STEADY-STATE SENSITIVITY OF THE CLIMATE MODEL

Doubling of the CO_2 concentration (with all other variables remaining unchanged) leads to absorption of an additional 4.4 W/m² of back radiation in the atmosphere, in general agreement with global climate model (GCM) results (Cess et al. 1993). The calculated increase in average global temperature for double CO_2 assuming a stretching factor *b* of 2.0, is 1.83°C, compared to warming of 1.5 to 4.5°C suggested by the GCMs (e.g., Cess et al. 1993).

The model response to 'equivalent' solar forcing – an increase of 4.4 W/m² in the planetary absorption of solar radiation – is 2.33°C. This is 27% higher than the response to CO_2 doubling because of differences in non-linear feedbacks caused by interactions involving water vapour, clouds, snow and ice. The sensitivity of 2.33°C/4.4Wm⁻²= 0.53°C/Wm⁻²is in reasonable agreement with Hoyt and Schatten's (1993) empirical estimate of 0.7°C/Wm⁻².

2.3 GREENHOUSE FORCING

One time-dependent model parameter is the greenhouse gas (GHG) concentration. The time dependence of the anthropogenic CO_2 concentrations used in the model is the same as that assumed by the Inter-governmental Panel on Climate Change (e.g., Shine et al. 1990; Siegenthaler and Sarmiento 1993). However, the logarithm of the CO_2 concentration was multiplied by a stretching factor, *b*, to include implicitly in the model not only CO_2 but also other greenhouse gases like methane, nitrous oxide, chlorofluorocarbons (e.g., Wang, et al. 1992). The stretching factor, *b*, is adjusted to obtain the best fit between the modelled to observed temperatures, either separately or in combination with the solar forcing.

2.4 SOLAR FORCING

Hoyt and Schatten 1993 (referred to below as HS93) offer an extensive discussion of proxies and models of secular changes in the global solar convective energy and the implied solar total irradiance changes. One of these proxies is the 'composite total irradiance change' based on five indicators – the sunspot cycle length, the envelope of sunspot number based on an 11-year running mean filter (Zhang et al. 1994), changes in solar equatorial rotation, fraction of penumbral spots, and decay rate of solar cycle. SPB96 identified the HS93 composite as the most probable best proxy for solar irradiance, based on its correlation with observed global temperature variations and on its satisfying the constraint of the 0.7% upper bound of maximum relative solar brightness change (Zhang et al. 1994).

We use a solar forcing function equal to the HS93 composite (which has an arbitrary scale) multiplied by a constant, such that the 1880-1993 range of solar brightness change in percentage equal to the stretching factor, *a* . The factor *a* is to be determined by requiring the best fit of the modelled temperature to the observed temperature, either separately or in combination with the GHG forcing.

2.5 RESULTS

For each of the five climate simulations performed in this study, either stretching factor *a*, or *b*, or both, were adjusted to maximise the fraction of the variance of observed temperature which can explained by the simulation. The results of these five simulations are depicted in Table 1 and in Figs. 1, 2, and 3.

Simulation A ignores solar forcing by setting stretching factor *a* equal to zero. A stretching factor *b* of 1.8 (Table 1, row A) produces the optimum fit between simulated and observed temperatures (Fig.1). This is in excellent agreement with Wang et al.'s (1992) scaling, which is equivalent to using a stretching factor *b* of 1.86. The simulated temperature changes over the 1885-1987 interval account for 63% of the observed temperature variance, and the maximum value of 0.55°C is the greater part of the observed maximum change of 0.72°C.

Simulation B is the reverse of A, ignoring the GHG forcing by setting *b* equal to zero, and finding a solar stretching factor *a* of 0.72 (Table 1, row B) to produce the optimum fit (Fig.1). This corresponds to a maximum solar irradiance change of 0.72% during the 1885-1987 interval. The simulated temperature changes over the 1885-1987 interval account for 78% of the observed temperature variance, and the maximum value of 0.57°C is the greater part of the observed maximum change of 0.72°C. Thus, solar brightness variations alone can account for somewhat more of the temperature variance and of the total temperature increase than GHG increases alone.

Forcing	Stretching factors		Explained Variance	DT_{max} (°C) (model)
	Solar (*a*)	GHG (*b*)	1885-1987	1885-1987
A. GHG alone	–	1.8	63%	0.55
B. Solar alone	0.72	–	78%	0.57
C. GHG & Solar	0.52	1.1	92%	0.64
D. GHG Part of C	–	1.1	51%	0.31
E. Solar Part of C	0.52	–	71%	0.41

The best fit solar stretching factor (*a*) is the maximum total irradiance change between 1885-1987. The best fit GHG stretching factor (*b*) is the multiplier of the logarithm of CO_2 concentration, used to include implicitly the radiative effect of other greenhouse gasses. Explained variance is the percentage of the variance of observed temperature explained by the best-fit climate simulation. DT_{max} may be compared with the observed value of 0.70°C.

Table 1: Summary of Temperature Simulations.

Model simulation of forcing by both GHG and solar forcing, simultaneously (Table 1, row C), results in an optimum fit (Fig. 2) for a GHG stretching factor *b* of 1.1, and a solar stretching factor *a*

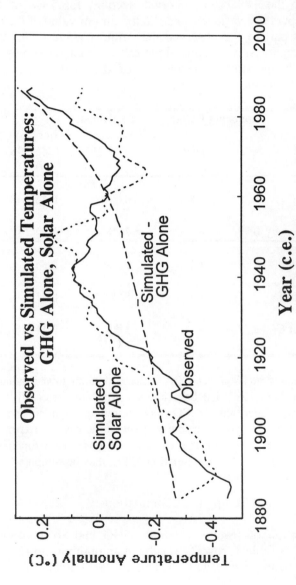

Figure 1: The solid curve represents the 11-year running mean of the observed global temperature anomalies from Hansen and Lebedeff (1987, 1988). Compare with optimum simulation for GHG forcing, alone, with no solar brightness changes (long dashes, corresponding to simulation A in Table 1), and with solar forcing, alone, with no GHG changes (short dashes, simulation B in Table 1).

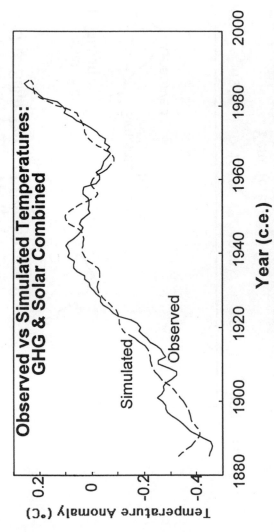

Figure 2: Same as Fig 1, but the one optimum simulation includes a combination of both GHG and solar forcing (dashed curve, simulation C in Table 1).

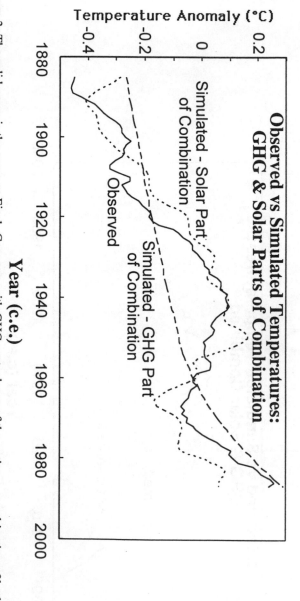

Figure 3: The solid curve is the same as Fig 1. Compare with GHG part, alone, of the optimum combination of both forcing functions, (long dashes, corresponding to simulation D in Table 1), and with the solar part, alone, of the combination (short dashes, simulation E in Table 1).

of 0.52. The simulated temperatures account for 92% of the observed temperature variance, and for a maximum change of 0.64°C in comparison with observed change of 0.72°C, in excellent agreement with observations. These results are, of course, better than forcing by either GHG variations or solar variations, alone. Comparing simulations B (Fig. 1) and C (Fig.2), it may also be noted that the added contribution from the GHG forcing is noticeable from 1970 onward, suggesting that the radiative forcing induced by anthropogenic greenhouse gasses has become non-negligible since the 1970s in our model.

An additional pair of simulations, D and E, was performed to examine the separate contributions of the GHG and solar parts of the simultaneous forcing in simulation C. The results (Table 1, rows D and E, and Fig. 3) show that solar forcing has had a somewhat greater role than GHG forcing in accounting for both the variance (71% compared to 51%) and maximum change (0.41°C compared to 0.31°C) of observed temperatures. This is consistent with the contrast between simulations A and B. In simulation D, the total temperature change was 0.31°C, while atmospheric CO_2 increased by a factor of 2 raised to the power 0.246, implying a climate sensitivity of 0.31°C/0.246 = 1.26°C/doubling-of-CO_2.

3. Statistical Study

As our second independent approach to evaluating the relative roles of solar and greenhouse forcing in climate variability, we use a standard multiple linear regression analysis between observed temperature (the dependent variable) and solar forcing and $\ln_2 (CO_2)$ (the independent variables). The regression coefficient for $\ln_2(CO_2)$ is 1.33°C/doubling-of- CO_2 in excellent agreement with the sensitivity of 1.26°C/doubling-of- CO_2. implied by model simulation D. The regression coefficient for solar forcing is 1.54°C per unit on HS93's arbitrary scale. Multiplying these regression coefficients by the ranges of the respective forcing function results in a 0.33°C effect of GHGs, and a 0.44°C effect of solar variations, whose sum, 0.77°C, is in excellent agreement with the observed range of 0.70°C during the interval 1880-1993.The multiple-correlation coefficient R^2 is 89.3%, which agrees quite well with the 92% of explained variance in simulation C. The statistical significance of this linear relationship may be determined by calculating:

$$\frac{R^2}{(1-R^2)} \times \frac{(N-K)}{(K-1)} = \frac{0.893}{(1-0.893)} \times \frac{(10-3)}{(3-1)} = 29.2$$

which is an F-distribution statistic (e.g., Bevington and Robinson 1992). with (K-1)=2, and (N-K) = (114/11-3) = 7 degrees of freedom. (The 114/11 is the record length divided by the smoothing filter length.) The 99 percentile of the F(2, 7) distribution is 9.55, which is far less than the sample F of 29.2, so one can confidently reject the null hypothesis that observed temperature variations are linearly independent of GHG and solar variations, especially the latter.

4. Conclusions

It appears from two independent analyses, one using a physically-based climate model, and the other a statistical model, that approximately 90% of the variation of global, annual temperature during the interval 1880-1993 can be explained on the basis of forcing by greenhouse gas changes and solar brightness variations, with the latter playing a somewhat larger role. The physical and statistical analyses suggest a climate sensitivity of 1.26 or 1.33°C/doubing-of-CO_2, respectively. Although the percentage of unexplained variance, *ca.* 10%, is quite low, and most likely due in large part to uncertainty in the data, it is possible that other physical processes, ignored in this study, deserve further investigation. These include volcanism, sulphate aerosols, and internal climate variability due to the non-linear interactions among the climate variables (e.g., Lorenz 1990; Posmentier 1990; Ghil 1991).

Acknowledgements

Our research was supported by the Electric Power Research Institute, and the Long Island University Faculty Research Released Time program.

References

Bevington, P. R. and Robinson, D.K. 1992: *Data Reduction and Error Analysis for The Physical Sciences*. New York: McGraw-Hill.

Cess, R. D. et al. 1993: Uncertainties in carbon dioxide radiative forcing in atmospheric general circulation models. *Science* **262**, 1252-1255.

Friis-Christensen, E. and Lassen, K. 1991: Length of the solar cycle: An indicator of solar activity closely associated with climate. *Science* **254**, 698-700.

Ghil, M. 1991: Quaternary glaciations: theory and observations. In *The Sun in Time* eds. C.P. Sonett, M. S. Giampapa, and M. S. Matthews, 511-542, Tucson: The University of Arizona Press.

Haigh, J.D. 1996: The impact of solar variability on climate. *Science* **272**, 981-984.

Hameed, S. and Gong, G. 1994: Variation of spring climate in lower-middle Yangtse river valley and its relation with solar-cycle length. *Geophys. Res. Let.* **21**, 2693-2696.

Hansen, J. and Lebedeff, S. 1987: Global trends of measured surface air temperature. *J. Geophys. Res.* **92D**, 13345-13372.

Hansen, J. and Lebedeff, S. 1988: Global surface air temperatures: Update through 1987. *Geophys. Res. Let.* **15**, 323-326.

Hoyt, D.V. and Schatten, K.H. 1993: A discussion of plausible solar irradiance variations, 1700-1992. *J. Geophys. Res.* **98**, 18895-18906.

Kelly, P.M. and Wigley, T.M.L. 1992: Solar cycle length, greenhouse forcing and global climate. *Nature* **360**, 328-330.

Lorenz, E. N. 1990: Can chaos and intransitivity lead to interannual variability? *Tellus* **42**, 378-389.

Michaels, P.J. and Knappenberger, P.C. 1996: Human effect on global climate? *Nature* **384**, 522-523.

Parker, D. E., Jones, P. D., Folland, C.K., and Bevan, A. 1994: Interdecadal changes of surface temperature since the late nineteenth century. *J. Geophys. Res.* **99**, 14373-14399.

Posmentier, E. S. 1990: Periodic, quasiperiodic, and chaotic behaviour in a non-linear toy climate model. *Annales Geophysicae* **8**, 781-790.

Posmentier, E. S. 1994: Response of an ocean-atmosphere climate model to Milankovic forcing. *Non-linear Processes in Geophysics* **1**, 26-30.

Reid, G. C. 1987: Influence of solar variability on global sea surface temperatures. *Nature* **329**, 142-143.

Reid, G. C. 1991. Solar total irradiance variations and the global sea surface temperature record. *J. Geophys. Res.* **96**, 2835-2844.

Santer, B. D., Taylor, K.E., Wigley, T.M.L., Johns, T.C., Jones, P. D., Karoly, D. J., Mitchell, J.F.B., Oort, A. H., Penner, J.E., Ramaswamy, V., Schwarzkopf, M. D., Stouffer, R.J., and Tett, S. 1996: A search for human influences on the thermal structure of the atmosphere. *Nature* **382**, 39-46.

Schatten, K.H. 1996: An atmospheric radiative-convective model: solar forcings. *The Astrophys. J. Let.* **460**, L69-L72.

Schlesinger, M. E. and Ramankutty, N. 1992: Implications for global warming of intercycle solar irradiance variation. *Nature* **360**, 330-333.

Shine, K.P., Derwent, R.G., Wuebbles, D. J., and Morcrette, J.J. 1990: Radiative forcing of climate. In *Climate Change: The IPCC Scientific Assessment* eds. J.T. Houghton et al., Cambridge: Cambridge University Press.

Siegenthaler, U. and Sarmiento, J.L. 1993: Atmospheric carbon dioxide and the ocean. *Nature* **365**, 119-125.

Soon, W.H., Posmentier, E. S., and Baliunas, S. L. 1996: Inference of solar irradiance variability from terrestrial temperature changes, 1880-1993: An astrophysical application of the Sun-Climate connection. *The Astrophys. J.* **472**, 891-902.

Tett, S.F.B., Mitchell, J.F.B., Parker, D. E., and Allen, M. R. 1996: Human influences on the vertical temperature structure: detection and observations. *Science* **274**, 1170-1173.

Tinsley, B. A., Hoeksema, J.T., and Baker, D.N. 1994: Stratospheric volcanic aerosols and changes in air-earth current density at solar wind magnetic sector boundaries as conditions for the Wilcox tropospheric vorticity effect. *J. Geophys. Res.* **99**, 16805-16813.

Wang, W.C., Dudek, M. P., and Liang, X.Z. 1992: Inadequacy of effective CO_2 as a proxy in assessing the regional climate change due to other radiatively active gases. *Geophys. Res. Let.* **19**, 1357-1378.

Weber, G.R. 1996: Human effect on global climate? *Nature* **384**, 523-524.

Zhang, Q., Soon, W.H., Baliunas, S. L., Lockwood, G.W., Skiff, B. A., and Radick, R.R. 1994: A method of determining possible brightness variations of the Sun in past centuries from observations of solar-type stars. *The Astrophys. J. Let.* **427**, L111-L114.

Eric Posmentier

Eric Posmentier is on the faculty of Long Island University, where he is currently Professor of Physics and Mathematics at the Brooklyn campus, after previous service at the Southampton campus as Professor and Chair of Marine Sciences, and of Physics and Mathematics. He is also a Visiting Professor of Earth Science at Dartmouth College. He has worked in seismology, atmospheric acoustics, estuarine oceanography, oceanic fine structure, and chaos theory; his present research is both in climate change and in quantum mechanics.

Willie Soon

Willie Soon is a physicist at the Solar and Stellar Physics Division of the Harvard-Smithsonian Center for Astrophysics. His current research investigations include a study in the variability of the magnetic and photometric activities on the surfaces of the Sun and other lower main sequence stars on time scales of decades to centuries, and their possible connection to long-term terrestrial climate change. Another theme to his research effort is the relative role of natural versus anthropogenic causes of climate change.

Sallie Baliunas

Sallie Baliunas is an astrophysicist at the Harvard-Smithsonian Center for Astrophysics. Dr. Baliunas also serves as Deputy Director of Mount Wilson Institute, and is a visiting professor at Tennessee State University. Her research interests include the evolution of surface magnetism and angular momentum in lower main sequence and post main sequence stars, and in particular, the past and future variations of brightness and magnetism of sun-like stars. She also studies stars using the new technology of high spatial resolution, adaptive optics.

Forecast of Global Temperature, El Niño, and Cloud Coverage by Astronomical Means

Theodor Landscheidt
Schroeter Institute for Research in Cycles of Solar Activity
Belle Côte, Nova Scotia
Canada

Summary

It is shown that middle-range variations in the global temperature, El Niño events, and minima in the intensity of cosmic rays accompanied by minima in global cloudiness can be explained and predicted by solar-terrestrial cycles connected with the sun's orbital motion about the centre of mass of the solar system.

Introduction

In my paper 'Global Warming or Little Ice Age?', published in this volume, I have described a semi-quantitative model that relates solar activity and climate to a fractal of solar cycles derived from the dynamics in the sun's orbital motion about the centre of mass of the solar system. Those who ignore all pieces of evidence pointing to the sun's variable activity as a main factor in climate change may try to dismiss the presented results as fortuitous. This will be difficult as the model has a physical background and covers a wide range of phenomena and time series of hundreds or even thousands of years. The best evidence for the proper function of the model are correct predictions based on it. So I will add some more forecasts to those already mentioned in 'Global Warming or Little Ice Age?' to expand the experimentum crucis.

Prediction of Global Temperature Variations Covering 3 – 4 Years

Forecasts in this range are considered impossible. The chaotic character of weather expressed in turbulence is thought to prevent predictions that go beyond several days. Yet practical results show that the solar factor is so strong that it forces cyclic patterns on the temperature. The prevailing mechanisms that create such a strong potential of solar forcing are not yet understood, but there are indications that stochastic resonance could be at work. It involves the co-operative interplay of random and periodic stimuli. Noise can improve the response to small periodic or quasi-periodic signals so that the small periodic input is able to entrain large-scale fluctuations (Moss, 1993; Wiesenfeld, 1993). There is plenty of noise in the atmosphere that could amplify periodic stimuli created by the sun's cyclic motion about the centre of mass of the solar system and the related variance in the sun's orbital angular momentum with its response in solar activity.

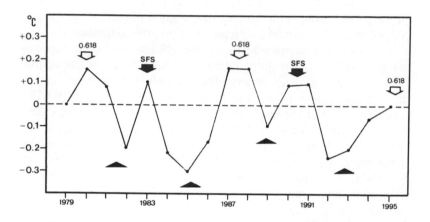

Figure 1: Mean global satellite-measured temperature 1979 – 1995. Positive and negative departures are related to the 1979 temperature as reference point. The filled arrows mark epochs of SFSs and the open arrows golden sections within cycles formed by consecutive SFSs. Both of these crucial phases consistently coincide with peaks of the positive departures. Midpoints between the open and filled arrows are indicated by flat triangles. They fall at troughs formed by negative departures. The next peak in positive departures is to be expected around 1998.6.

Time series of 'world temperature' used by IPCC scientists are affected by shortcomings related to station homogeneity, spatial coverage, time coverage, and subjective estimates (Corbyn and Golipour, 1996). So I make use of objective satellite data first published by Spencer and Christy (1990). This time series of truly global temperature data of the lower troposphere, shown in Figure 1, begins in 1979.

The measurements are thought to be accurate within ±0.01°C. The positive or negative departures are measured from the global temperature average of the years 1982-1991. Contrary to the IPCC predictions of global warming due to greenhouse enhancement the satellite data indicate no net warming at all, but rather a cooling trend. The curve in Figure 1 shows a quasi-cyclic pattern. It is correlated with the fractal of solar cycles described in my paper 'Global Warming or Little Ice Age?'. The filled arrows mark starts of small fingers (SFS) related to minima of the 3-year running variance in the sun's orbital angular momentum. They occur when the sun's centre, the centre of mass of the solar system, and Jupiter – the biggest of the giant planets – are in line. Both of the SFSs coincide with peaks of positive departures.

The open arrows designate the golden section in between consecutive SFSs. The golden mean divides a frame structure like a line segment, a cycle, or any other delimited feature so that the ratio of the whole (1) to the larger part, called major (0.618), equals the ratio of the larger part (0.618) to the smaller one, called minor (0.3819). The value 0.618 is termed the golden number G. The major of the golden section within a cycle is found by multiplying the length of the cycle by 0.618. The stability of dynamical systems including the solar system and atoms or molecules hinges on the golden section (Kolmolmogorov, 1979; Arnold, 1963; Moser, 1973; Child, 1993). I have shown (Landscheidt, 1995) that the golden section in addition plays an important role in all kinds of natural cycles from the 11-year sunspot cycle and the magnetic Hale-cycle to dozens of climatic cycles. Figure 1 is another confirmation. All of the golden section phases 0.618 in between consecutive SFSs forming cycles of a special length fall at peaks of the positive departures. The overall correlation between the temperature peaks and the aggregate of SFSs and golden sections is rather close. Interestingly, this changes when we look at global temperature data used by the IPCC. The peak in 1980 then shifts to 1981 and the 0.618 phase is no longer close to the peak. This seems to indicate a more reliable quality of the satellite data. The flat filled triangles in Figure 1 mark midpoints between the epochs indicated by open or filled arrows. All of them fall at troughs formed by negative departures though the correlation is not as close as with peaks. Remarkably, the SFSs and golden sections match the temperature peaks in spite of their widely varying intervals. The connection is so promising

174

that it seems solid enough to support a forecast experiment. The next temperature peak in the satellite data is to be expected around 1998.6, the epoch of the coming SFS, and the next temperature trough should form around 1997.0, the midpoint between the 0.618-phase in 1995.4 and the SFS in 1998.6. Probably, the observed epoch of the trough will not be as close to the mark as the observed epoch of the peak.

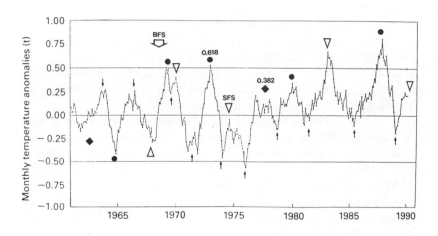

Figure 2: Monthly sea surface and land air temperature anomalies 1961 – 1989 for the tropical zone extending from 20º N to 20º S, after Houghton et al.,(1990). Strong peaks indicate ENSO events (El Niño + Southern Oscillation). As explained in the text, all maxima and minima in the curve are related to crucial phases in solar-terrestrial cycles derived from the sun's orbital motion about the center of mass of the solar system. The computability of these phases makes predictions of El Niño events possible.

Prediction of El Niño

The relationship between SFSs, golden section phases within cycles formed by consecutive SFSs, and global temperature, presented in Figure 1, is not an isolated solar-terrestrial feature. The connection presented in Figure 2 (from IPCC, 1990) is a further example. It solves a seemingly intractable problem of climatology and meteorology: the prediction of El Niño. This phenomenon represents a cyclic large scale atmosphere-ocean interaction which has climatic effects throughout the Pacific region and far beyond.

It is the only true global-scale oscillation that has been identified so far and is also called the ENSO event because of its links with the Southern Oscillation, a fluctuation of the intertropical atmospheric oscillation. Every three to seven years normally cold waters over the entire eastern equatorial Pacific Ocean show a dramatic warming of several degrees Celsius which are associated with very large anomalies in the global weather. The inhibition of the upwelling of nutrient-rich cold waters causes the death of a large proportion of the plankton population and a strong decline in the numbers of surface fish, especially anchovies. Birds and tuna, which depend on small fish for food, leave or die. The gas from decaying fish and birds is said to be so powerful that it can blacken the paint of ships passing by. These conditions do tremendous damage to the Peruvian economy.

The curve in Figure 2 plots the monthly sea surface and land air temperature anomalies between 1961-1989 for the tropical zone extending from 20° N to 20° S. The stronger peaks indicate ENSO events. After the BFS of 1968, marked by a big open arrow, all SFSs, designated by open triangles, coincide with peaks in the plot. The same is true for the majority of the golden section within cycles formed by consecutive SFSs. These 0.618-phases are indicated by filled circles. In case of SFSs longer than eight years also the minor of the golden section goes along with peaks. These 0.382-phases are marked by filled diamonds. Troughs in the time series are rather exactly linked to midpoints in between consecutive crucial phases, designated by small arrows. Before the nodal phase of a big finger in 1968, the pattern was reversed. SFSs, as well as majors and minors within small finger cycles, coincided with troughs, and the midpoints between these phases went along with peaks. This is another example of phase reversal induced by nodal points in cycles higher up in the hierarchy of the fractal of solar cycles, as described in my paper 'Global Warming or Little Ice Age?'. The relationship presented in Figure 1 should also be subjected to such phase reversal due to BFSs in 1933, 1968, and 2007. The SF-cycle running from SFS 1990.3 to SFS 1998.6 is longer than 8 years. Thus, the minor in 1993, the major in 1995 and the SFS in 1998 should coincide with peaks in the monthly temperature anomalies. The 1993 peak materialised punctually. In my paper on the physical function of the golden section (Landscheidt, 1995), written in early 1995, I had predicted another El Niño event for 1995 though such a close sequence of El Niños was unusual. The forecast proved correct (Fu et al., 1996).

Forecast of Global Cloud Coverage

IPCC scientists dismiss the sun's variable activity as irrelevant. They argue that the sun's influence, if there is any, is by far too small to have any effect. The contrary is true. The sun's role in climate change is so dominant that the greenhouse effect due to carbon dioxide enhancement may be dismissed as irrelevant. The weakest point in the IPCC-models is the role of cloud radiative interactions. A NASA multi-satellite experiment has determined that clouds cool the planet more than they heat it and identified them as a major source of uncertainty in three-dimensional circulation models used for studying the greenhouse effect and global warming. The global mean long-wave and short-wave cloud forcing are both larger than the trace gas forcing by a factor of 15 to 20. The short-wave effect (albedo) shifts the system to a cooler climate, while the long-wave effect (absorption) causes a warmer climate. The Earth Radiation Budget Experiment (ERBE) data show that in the present climate the short-wave forcing is stronger and generates a net cooling of at least -17 W/m^2 (Ramanathan et al., 1989).

If there is a connection between solar variability, cloud cover, and global temperature, it can only be traced if there are global measurements of the area of the sky covered by clouds. Only satellites can provide such global data of the earth's cloudiness. The International Satellite Cloud Climatology Project (ISCCP) has collected just these data for the period July 1983 to December 1990 (Rossow and Schiffer, 1991). Svensmark and Friis-Christensen (1996) took the homogeneous observations made by geostationary s over the oceans and compared them with the varying intensity of cosmic rays which show a negative correlation with the sunspot activity in the 11-year cycle. Figure 3 presents the result. The thick curve plots the 12-month running average of the global cloud cover expressed as changes in per cent (left scale). The thin curve presents the monthly mean counting rates of neutrons measured by the ground-based monitor in Climax, Colorado (right scale). The observations of other neutron monitors like those in Huancayo, Deep River, Calgary, or Moscow show nearly the same results. Neutron monitors provide an indirect count of cosmic rays, since the primary cosmic rays create secondary neutron emission when they collide with molecules or atoms in the atmosphere. The correlation between the two curves

177

in Figure 3 is close ($r = 0.95$). According to Svensmark and Friis-Christensen the parallel course continues in the years after 1990. If the effect is real, the response of cloud cover to cosmic ray flux should be weaker close to the geomagnetic equator where the horizontal field lines of the geomagnetic field form a stronger shield against impinging ionising particles. Svensmark and Friis-Christensen have shown that just this weaker response is observed. Short-term responses were also observed, especially after Forbush decreases – sudden decreases in cosmic ray intensity caused by energetic solar eruptions which in some cases generate solar cosmic rays.

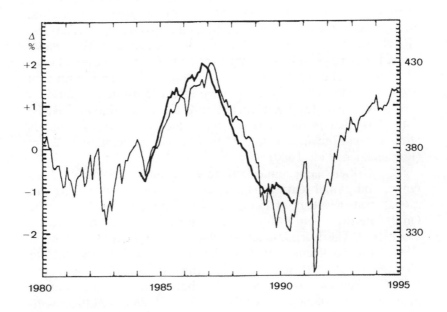

Figure 3: The thin curve plots the monthly means of counting rates observed by the neutron monitor Climax, Colorado, an indirect measure of the intensity of cosmic rays. The thick curve shows 12-month running means of the change of global cloud cover in per cent based on observations of geo-stationary satellites over the oceans. The parallel course of the curves points to a close connection between cosmic rays, solar activity, and global cloudiness.

Figure 3 shows that strong cosmic rays go along with more clouds and weak cosmic rays with less clouds. It is evident that the global cloud cover decreased by more than 3 per cent from its highest peak at the end of 1986 to its deepest point in 1990. According to

178

Svensmark and Friis-Christensen (1996) this is equivalent to an increase in irradiance of 0.8 to 1.7 W/m². An effect of this order is quite remarkable, since the total radiative forcing by carbon dioxide accumulated since 1750 has been estimated by the IPCC (1995) not to go beyond 1.5 W/m². Ramanathan et al. (1989) give the value 1.3 W/m² for the period 1850 to 1985. This means that cosmic rays, modulated by the sun's variable activity, achieve an effect within three and a half years for which the accumulation of carbon dioxide in the atmosphere needs more than a century. This shows clearly to what extent the greenhouse effect has been overestimated in comparison with the solar contribution to climate change which turns out to be the most important factor. There is also a physical explanation of the effect: the secondary ions produced by the primary cosmic rays may serve as condensation nuclei with hygroscopic properties that enhance the formation of clouds (Dickinson, 1975; Franke, 1969).

There is a coarse negative correlation between cosmic rays and the 11-year sunspot cycle. Minima in the intensity of cosmic rays occur around sunspot maxima and vice versa. This inverse relationship seems to offer a means to predict the course of cosmic rays and the related cloud cover. Yet this is not so. Attempts of astronomers to predict the epochs of maxima in the 11-year sunspot cycle have shown how difficult this is. Eleven years is only the mean length of the cycle; the individual length varies between 7 and 17 years. Yet even if it were possible to predict 11-year sunspot maxima precisely, this would not imply exact predictions of the epochs of minima in the intensity of cosmic rays. The primary cause of the solar modulation of cosmic rays is not the number of sunspots, but the varying strength of the solar wind. This supersonic outflow of plasma originates in the very hot corona of the sun and carries ionised particles and magnetic field lines from the sun. It reaches velocities between 300 and 1000 km/s. While it is expanding towards the boundary of the solar system, cosmic ray particles interacting with it lose energy. When the solar wind blows heavily, cosmic rays become weak, and when the solar wind is in a lull, cosmic rays are strong. The variation in the strength of the solar wind does not closely follow the rhythm of the 11-year sunspot cycle. The fastest solar wind with velocities of about 1000 km/s emanates from coronal holes with open magnetic field structures the activity of which is not correlated with the number of sunspots. The highest velocities in the solar wind of up to 2500 km/s are generated by energetic solar eruptions (solar flares and eruptive prominences) which even contribute to cosmic rays. These solar cosmic rays have an impact on the strength of the solar wind, but show fluctuations different from the galactic cosmic rays that enter the solar system from the outside. Energetic solar eruptions shun sunspot maxima and even occur close to sunspot minima.

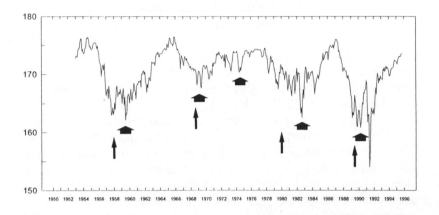

Figure 4:   Counting rates 1953 – 1995 observed by the neutron monitor Huancayo, from Solar-Geophysical Data, (1995). Maxima in the 11-year sunspot cycle are marked by long arrows. Epochs of SFSs are indicated by short arrows. SFSs show a closer connection with deep minima in the intensity of cosmic rays than sunspot maxima and open a possibility of predictions, as their epochs can be computed. These predictions also apply to minima in global cloudiness because of their close relationship with cosmic ray minima.

Thus Figure 4 is no longer a surprise. The curve shows the cosmic ray intensity measured by the neutron monitor Huancayo. The data go back to 1953. Maxima of sunspot activity in the 11-year cycle are indicated by long arrows. It is easy to see that in three of the four covered cases the sunspot maxima reach a distance of two to three years from the deep cosmic ray minima, which is a considerable deviation from the crucial epochs. The short fat arrows mark the epochs of SFSs. Obviously, they are much closer to the mark. Yet their decisive advantage is that they can be predicted, as they are computable. Thus, the next deep cosmic ray minimum may be expected around 1998.6, the epoch of the coming SFS. The time series of neutron monitor data, that the connection is based on, is rather short. Yet the diversity and dependability of the solar-terrestrial function of SFSs seems to justify a prediction experiment. The results published by Svensmark and Friis-Christensen imply that the minimum in the intensity of cosmic rays will go along with a decreased cloudiness.

The unusually steep drop in cosmic rays down to count rates around 155 in 1991, clearly visible in Figure 4, is an example of the important role of solar cosmic rays. It was caused by a huge proton flare in March 1991 which produced more cosmic rays than the previous solar cycle in total. In my paper 'Global Warming or Little Ice Age?' I have shown that it is linked to a very rare retrograde phase in the sun's motion about the centre of mass of the solar system. The next retrograde phase will occur in 2169 and should again go along with spectacular eruptional activity on the sun. Yet who will check this forecast?

References

Arnold, W. I. 1963. Small denominators and problems of stability of motion in classical and celestial mechanics. *Russian Mathematical Survey*, 18, 85.

Child, M. S. 1993. Non-linearity and chaos in atoms and molecules. In T. Mullin ed. *The Nature of chaos*, 261-281. Oxford: Clarendon Press.

Corbyn, P. and Golipour, M. 1996. What is global Temperature? The Inadequacy of estimation methods. In ESEF *The Global Warming Debate*, 80-86.Cambridge: European Science and Environment Forum.

Dickinson, R. E. 1975. Solar variability and the lower atmosphere. *Bull. Am. Meteorol. Soc.*, 56, 1240.

Franke, H. 1969. *Lexikon der Physik*, 845. Stuttgart: Franckh'sche Verlagshandlung.

Fu, L. L., Koblinsky, C. J., Minster, J. F., and Picaut, J. 1996. Reflecting on the first three years of TOPEX/POSEIDON. *EOS*, 77, no.12, March 19, 109, 111, 117.

IPCC 1990: Houghton, J. T., Jenkins, G. J., and Ephraums, J. J. eds. *Climatic Change: The IPCC scientific assessment*. Cambridge: Cambridge University Press.

Kolmogorov, A. N. 1979. Preservation of conditionally periodic movements with small change in the Hamiltonian function. *Lecture Notes in Physics*, 93, 51.

Landscheidt, T. 1995. Die kosmische Funktion des Goldenen Schnitts. In P. Richter ed. *Sterne, Mond, Kometen. Festschrift zum 75. Jahrestag der Gründung der Olbers-Gesellschaft Bremen*, 240-276. Bremen: H. M. Hauschild.

Moser, J. 1973. *Stable and random motions in dynamical systems*. Princeton: Princeton University Press.

Moss, F. 1993. Stochastic resonance. In G. H. Weiss ed.. *Some problems in statistical physics*. Philadelphia: SIAM.

Ramanathan, V., Barkstrom, B. R., and Harrison, E. 1989. Climate and the earth's radiation budget. *Physics Today* (May 1989): 22-32

Rossow, W. and Schiffer, R. 1991. ISCCP cloud data products. *Bull. Am. Meteor. Soc.*, 72, 2-20.

Spencer, R. W. and Christy, J. R. 1990. *Science*, 247, 1558.

Solar-Geophysical-Data, prompt reports, December 1995, 616, 116. Boulder: National Oceanic and Atmospheric Administration.

Svensmark, H. and Friis-Christensen, E. 1996. Variation of cosmic ray flux and global cloud coverage – a missing link in solar-climate relationship. Invited paper presented at the COSPAR96 space science conference at the University of Birmingham, submitted to the *Journal of Atmospheric and Terrestrial Physics*.

Wiesenfeld, K. 1993. An introduction to stochastic resonance. In J. R. Buchler and H. E. Kandrup eds. *Stochastic Processes in Astrophysics*, 13-25. New York: New York Academy of Sciences.

Theodor Landscheidt

Dr Landscheidt graduated from Göttingen University in 1955. He is director of the Schroeter Institute for Research in Cycles of Solar Activity, and is on the board of directors of the International Committee for Research in Environmental Factors of the Free University of Brussels. He has published many papers on solar-climatic relationships and is engaged in the prediction of solar activity and its terrestrial responses.

Carbon cycle modelling and the residence time of natural and anthropogenic atmospheric CO_2: on the construction of the 'Greenhouse Effect Global Warming' dogma.

Tom V. Segalstad
Mineralogical-Geological Museum
University of Oslo
Norway

> When you have eliminated the impossible,
> whatever remains, however improbable, must be the
> truth.
>
> Sir Arthur Conan Doyle (1859-1930).

Summary

The United Nations Intergovernmental Panel on Climate Change (IPCC) has offered three forms of evidence that the apparent contemporary atmospheric CO_2 increase is anthropogenic. These are discussed and rejected: CO_2 measurements from ice cores; CO_2 measurements in air; and carbon isotope data in conjunction with carbon cycle modelling.

It is shown why the ice core method and its results must be rejected and that current air CO_2 measurements are not validated and their results subjectively 'edited'. Further it is shown that carbon cycle modelling based on non-equilibrium models, remote from observed reality and chemical laws, made to fit non-representative data through the use of non-linear ocean evasion 'buffer' correction factors constructed from a pre-conceived idea, constitute a circular argument with no scientific validity.

Both radioactive and stable carbon isotopes show that the real atmospheric CO_2 residence time (lifetime) is only about 5 years, and that the maximum amount of fossil-fuel CO_2 in the atmosphere is only 4%. Any CO_2 level rise beyond this can only come from a much larger, but natural, carbon reservoir with much

*higher 13-C/12-C isotope ratio than that of the fossil fuel pool,
namely from the ocean, and/or the lithosphere, and/or the Earth's
interior.*

*The apparent annual atmospheric CO_2 level increase,
postulated to be anthropogenic, would constitute only some 0.2%
of the total annual amount of CO_2 exchanged naturally between
the atmosphere and the ocean plus other natural sources and
sinks. It is more probable that such a small ripple in the annual
natural flow of CO_2 would be caused by natural fluctuations of
geophysical processes.*

*13-C/12-C isotope mass balance calculations show that
the IPCC's atmospheric residence time of 50-200 years makes the
atmosphere too light (50% of its current CO_2 mass) to fit its
measured 13-C/12-C isotope ratio. This explains why IPCC's
incorrect model creates its artificial 50% 'missing sink'. This
'missing sink' of about 3 giga-tonnes carbon annually should have
led all governments to question and probably to reject the IPCC's
model. When such rejection has not yet occurred, it beautifully
shows the result of the 'scare-them-to-death' influence principle.*

*The IPCC uses invalid presumptions and an unrealistic
carbon cycle modelling which simply does not reflect reality and,
if true, would make impossible the existence of carbonated beer or
soda 'pop' as we know it.*

1. Introduction

Atmospheric CO_2 is as important as oxygen for life on Earth.
Without CO_2 the plant photosynthetic metabolism would not be
possible, and the present life-forms on Earth would vanish. In
recent years a dogma has been constructed that an apparent
increase in atmospheric CO_2 concentration is caused by
anthropogenic burning of fossil carbon in the forms of petroleum,
coal, and natural gas. This extra atmospheric CO_2 has been
claimed to cause global climatic change with a significant
atmospheric temperature rise of 1.5 to 4.5°C in the next century
(Houghton et al., 1990).

There is then indeed a paradox that CO_2, 'The Gas of
Life', is now being condemned as the evil 'polluting' gas, a gas
which will be a threat to life on Earth, through a postulated
'Global Warming'. This appears all the more paradoxical when
earlier warmer periods in the Earth's history are characterized as
'Climatic Optimum'. The construction of what may be called the
'CO_2 Greenhouse Effect Global Warming' dogma, based on
atmospheric CO_2 level measurements in air and ice cores, carbon

185

cycle modelling, CO_2 residence time (lifetime is here used synonymously), and carbon isotopes, is examined in this paper.

2. The construction of dogmas

In the natural sciences, scientific method is based on the testing of hypotheses with the help of (1) empirical observations, (2) laboratory experiments, and (3) theory based on these. If the three parts concur and the theory is robust enough to predict results which will be compatible with new observations and experiments, then we have found a hypothesis with high significance. With further testing this hypothesis may be deemed to be a law of nature, which in turn can be used to reject other hypotheses not supported by observations and experiments. It is of course fundamental that all three major parts of the scientific method be based on sound statistical procedures regarding sampling theory, data representation, significance, error propagation, causality, etc., and should be unbiased and free of advocacy. If any part of the evidence does not support the hypothesis, the hypothesis should be rejected (Churchman, 1948).

Over the last years, mainly after the fall of communism, environmentalism seems to have taken the vacant place on the political scene. This new 'ism' alleges that Man is destructive, unnatural, evil, and guilty of destroying the environment. The 'proofs' used in this respect are based on selected science, in many cases not based on the objectivity of the scientific method of natural sciences (Sanford, 1992). We see that most often the treatment of what is normal or natural is lacking from the environmental 'dooms', and that we only are told what is 'abnormal' or 'unnatural' without an indisputable baseline reference.

To construct a dogma, the methodology is to start with an idea one feels to be correct and then find evidence to support it. Reason will then have to be substituted by intuition, belief, faith, emotions, or feelings as the ultimate source of knowledge. Sanford (1992) further points out that the 'ecosopher' Arne Næss (1990) begins a book with the section "Beginning with intuitions" and a feeling of 'our world in crisis'. The dogma will be accepted as truth by the people at large if it is supported by "authorities", "experts", and well-known important people, not necessarily with their expertise in the relevant field; and especially so if the dogma is also supported by international bodies or assemblies, and given a wide and one-sided coverage by the media. The dogma will probably be more successful if it is a self-fulfilling prophecy.

186

The marketing and influence, i.e. the psychology of persuasion of a dogma, will therefore be important for it to be accepted as truth. People are usually not able to use all relevant information available. They use instead only a single, highly representative piece of the relevant information. When something is presented as a scary scenario, it creates an emotional reaction that makes it difficult to think straight (i.e. consider all facts), especially if a belief has been created that decisions regarding a common crisis will have to be made fast (Cialdini, 1993). This is what has been called the 'scare-them-to-death' approach (Böttcher, 1996), and makes the foundation for creating a doomsday dogma. Stephen Schneider, a climatologist and leading proponent of the global warming theory, says: "To capture the public imagination ... we have to offer up some scary scenarios, make simplified dramatic statements and little mention of any doubts one might have", thereby acting as an advocate for his subjective belief in the 'Greenhouse Effect Global Warming' dogma rather than as an objective scientist (Sanford, 1992).

A doomsday dogma made under these conditions will very likely cause political turmoil. The old saying 'Everybody talks about the weather, and nobody does anything about it' is claimed to be invalid when burning fossil fuel will allegedly change the world's climates. The creation of a 'CO_2 Greenhouse Effect Global Warming' dogma enables political authorities to appropriate resources by taxing energy and centralise power in government departments.

3. The foundation of the CO_2 dogma – early atmospheric CO_2 measurements

In order to construct a 'CO_2 Greenhouse Effect Global Warming' dogma, it will be necessary to justify that (1) pre-industrial atmospheric CO_2 was lower than today, (2) atmospheric CO_2 has steadily risen from its pre-industrial level to today's level, (3) burning fossil fuel is causing an increase in atmospheric CO_2 level, (4) hence atmospheric CO_2 must have a long residence time (lifetime), and (5) atmospheric temperatures are increasing due to Man's burning of fossil fuel.

Callendar (1938) revived the hypothesis of 'Greenhouse Warming' due to human activity, proposed by Arrhenius (1896). Callendar may truly be regarded as the father of the current dogma on anthropogenic global warming (Jaworowski et al., 1992 b). In order to support his hypothesis, Callendar (1940, 1958) selected atmospheric CO_2 data from the 19th and 20th centuries. Fonselius et al. (1956) showed that the raw data ranged randomly between about 250 and 550 ppmv (parts per million by volume) during this time period, but by selecting the data carefully, Callendar was able to present a steadily rising trend from about 290 ppmv for the period 1866 – 1900, to 325 ppmv in 1956.

Callendar was strongly criticized by Slocum (1955), who demonstrated a strong bias in Callendar's data selection method. Slocum pointed out that it was statistically impossible to find a trend in this set of raw data, and that the total data set showed a constant average of about 335 ppmv over this period from the 19th to the 20th century. Bray (1959) also criticized the selection method of Callendar, who rejected values 10% or more different from the 'general average', the more so because Callendar's 'general average' was neither defined nor given.

Note that Callendar (1940) wrote: "There is, of course, no danger that the amount of CO_2 in the air will become uncomfortably large because as soon as the excess pressure in the air becomes appreciable, say about 0.0003 atmos., the sea will be able to absorb this gas as fast as it is likely to be produced."

Callendar (1949) repeated this fact, but went on to say: "As the deep waters of the sea move slowly and only shallow contact surface is involved in the carbon-dioxide equilibrium, this reservoir does not immediately control a sudden eruption of the gas such as has occurred this century. It will be hundreds or perhaps thousands of years before the sea absorbs its fair share." Callendar believed that nearly all the CO_2 produced by fossil fuel combustion has remained in the atmosphere. He suggested that the increase in atmospheric CO_2 may account for the observed slight rise in average temperature in northern latitudes during the recent decades.

The CO_2 dogma was given further impetus by Revelle & Suess (1957) who wrote: "Thus human beings are now carrying out a large scale geophysical experiment of a kind which could not have happened in the past nor be reproduced in the future. Within a few centuries we are returning to the air and oceans the concentrated organic carbon stored over hundreds of millions of years." But by considering the chemical facts on the exchange of CO_2 between the atmosphere and the ocean, they concluded that only a total increase of 20 to 40% in atmospheric CO_2 can be anticipated by burning all fossil fuel. This is comparable to the 20% increase calculated by Segalstad from the air/sea CO_2 partition coefficient given by chemical equilibrium constants (1996).

At the same time Craig (1957) pointed out from the natural (by cosmic rays) radiocarbon (14-C) production rate that atmospheric CO_2 is in active exchange with very large CO_2 reservoirs in the ocean and biosphere. However, Callendar (1958) had apparently more faith in his carefully selected CO_2 data, because he glossed Craig's conclusion by writing: "Thus, if the increase shown by the measurements discussed here is even approximately representative of the whole atmosphere, it means that the oceans have not been accepting additional CO_2 on anything like the expected scale."

4. The building of the dogma – recent atmospheric CO_2 measurements

The selectivity of the atmospheric CO_2 data selected by Callendar made it necessary to start compiling analytical data of contemporary atmospheric CO_2. 19 North-European stations measured atmospheric CO_2 over a 5-year period from 1955 to 1959. Measured with a wet-chemical technique, the atmospheric CO_2 level was found to vary between approximately 270 and 380 ppmv, with annual means of $315 - 331$ ppmv, and there was no tendency of rising or falling atmospheric CO_2 level at any of the 19 stations during this 5-year period (Bischof, 1960). The data are particularly important because they are unselected and therefore free of potential biases from selection procedures, unlike the CO_2 measurements based on the procedures at Mauna Loa (see below). Note that these measurements were taken in an industrial region, and would indeed have shown an increase in CO_2 levels if increasing amounts of anthropogenic CO_2 were accumulating in the atmosphere during this period.

During the same period atmospheric CO_2 measurements were started near the top of the strongly CO_2-emitting (e.g., Ryan, 1995) Hawaiian Mauna Loa volcano. The reason for the choice of location was that it should be far away from CO_2-emitting industrial areas. At the Mauna Loa Observatory the measurements were taken with a new infra-red (IR) absorbing instrumental method, never validated versus the accurate wet chemical techniques. Criticism has also been directed to the analytical methodology and sampling error problems (Jaworowski et al., 1992 a; and Segalstad, 1996, for further references), and the fact that the results of the measurements were 'edited' (Bacastow et al., 1985); large portions of raw data were rejected, leaving just a small fraction of the raw data subjected to averaging techniques (Pales & Keeling, 1965).

The acknowledgement in the paper by Pales & Keeling (1965) describes how the Mauna Loa CO_2 monitoring programme started:

> The Scripps program to monitor CO_2 in the atmosphere and oceans was conceived and initiated by Dr. Roger Revelle who was director of the Scripps Institution of Oceanography while the present work was in progress. Revelle foresaw the geochemical implications of the rise in atmospheric CO_2 resulting from fossil fuel combustion, and he sought means to ensure that this "large scale geophysical experiment", as he termed it, would be adequately documented as it occurred. During all stages of the present work Revelle was mentor, consultant, antagonist. He shared with us his broad knowledge of earth science and appreciation for the oceans and atmosphere as they really exist, and he inspired us to keep in sight the objectives which he had originally persuaded us to accept.

This may not live up to the highest ideals of a research programme.

The annual mean CO_2 level as reported from Mauna Loa for 1959 was 315.83 ppmv (15 ppmv lower than the contemporaneous North-European average level), reportedly rising steadily to 351.45 in January 1989 (Keeling et al., 1989), by averaging large daily and seasonal variations (the significance of all their data points is not justified), but still within the range of the North European measurements 30-35 years earlier. Hence a rise in global atmospheric CO_2 level has not yet been significantly justified by validated methods and sound statistics.

5. Setting the dogma baseline – CO_2 measurements in ice cores

In order to show that recent atmospheric CO_2 levels have risen due to the burning of fossil fuel, it was necessary to show a significant level increase above pre-industrial CO_2 levels. We saw how Callendar was able to set a baseline of about 290 ppmv by rejecting values deviating more than 10% from his desired value.

It was believed that snow accumulating on ice sheets would preserve the contemporaneous atmosphere trapped between snowflakes during snowfalls, so that the CO_2 content of air inclusions in cores from ice sheets should reveal paleoatmospheric CO_2 levels. Jaworowski et al. (1992 b) compiled all such CO_2 data available, finding that CO_2 levels ranged from 140 to 7,400 ppmv. However, such paleoatmospheric CO_2 levels published after 1985 were never reported to be higher than 330 ppmv. Analyses (Neftel at al., 1982) from the more than 2,000 m deep Byrd ice core (Antarctica), showed unsystematic values ranging from about 190 to 420 ppmv. These values were falsely 'filtered' when the alleged same data showed a rising trend from about 190 ppmv (35,000 years ago) to about 290 ppmv (Callendar's pre-industrial baseline at 4,000 years ago) when re-reported in 1988 (Neftel et al., 1988); shown by Jaworowski et al. (1992 b) in their Fig. 5.

Siegenthaler & Oeschger (1987) were going to make "model calculations that are based on the assumption that the atmospheric $[CO_2]$ increase is due to fossil CO_2 input" and other human activities. For this modelling they constructed a composite diagram of CO_2 level data from Mauna Loa and the Siple (Antarctica) core (see Jaworowski et al., 1992 b, Fig. 10). The data from the Siple core (Neftel et al., 1985) showed the 'best' data in terms of a rising CO_2 trend. Part of the reason for this was that the core partially melted across the Equator during transportation before it was analysed (Etheridge et al., 1988), but this was neither mentioned by the analysts nor the researchers later using the data (see Jaworowski et al., 1992 b). Rather it was characterized as "the excellent quality of the ice core" and its CO_2 concentration data "are assumed to represent the global mean concentration history and used as input data to the model" (Siegenthaler & Oeschger, 1987). The two CO_2 level curves were constructed to overlap each other, but they would not match at corresponding age.

In order to make a matching construction between the two age-different non-overlapping curves, it was necessary to make the assumption that the age of the gas inclusion air would have to be 95 years younger than the age of the enclosing ice. But this was not mentioned by the originators Siegenthaler & Oeschger (1987). This artificial construction has been used as a basis for numerous speculative models of changes in the global carbon cycle.

Oeschger et al. (1985) postulated this "air younger than enclosing ice" thesis from an explanation that the upper 70 m of the ice sheets would be open to air circulation until the gas cavities were sealed. Jaworowski et al. (1992 b) rejected this postulate on the basis that air is constantly driven out of the snow, firn, and ice strata during the snow-to-ice compression and metamorphism, so that ice deeper than about 1,000 m will have lost all original air inclusions. Deep ice cores will fracture when they are taken to the surface, and ambient air will be trapped in new, secondary inclusions. Both argon-39 and krypton-85 isotopes show that large amounts of ambient air are indeed included in the air inclusions in deep ice cores, and air that from the inclusions will not be representative of paleoatmospheres (Jaworowski et al., 1992 b).

Contamination from drilling fluids and more than twenty physical-chemical processes occurring in the ice before, during, and after drilling, make ice cores unsuitable for paleoatmospheric work (Jaworowski et al., 1992 b).

The most famous ice core, the Vostok (Antarctica) core, with air inclusions allegedly representing the global paleoatmospheres over the last 160,000 years, show CO_2 levels below 200 ppmv for many tens of thousands of years spanning 30,000 to 110,000 years BP (Barnola et al., 1987). "Most geochemists were convinced that changes such as these could not occur", says Sarmiento (1991) about these low alleged paleoatmospheric CO_2 levels. Such low atmospheric CO_2 levels below approximately 250 ppmv (McKay et al., 1991) would have led to extinction of certain plant species. This has not been recorded by paleobotanists, showing clearly that the ice core CO_2 results are not representative of paleoatmospheres (Jaworowski et al., 1992 b), hence the CO_2 ice-core method and its results must be rejected.

6. Justifying the dogma – carbon cycle modelling vs. reality

The Intergovernmental Panel on Climate Change (IPCC) uses 'carbon cycle modelling' as part of one of their 3 evidences that the observed atmospheric CO_2 increase is indeed anthropogenic (Houghton et al., 1990; page 14, Section 1.2.5 called "Evidence that the contemporary carbon dioxide increase is anthropogenic", last sentence: "qualitatively consistent with results from carbon cycle modelling").

The former chairman of IPCC, Bert Bolin, first published a paper on this topic with Eriksson in 1959. Here they expand on the belief of Callendar (1958) that his apparent atmospheric CO_2 increase must be anthropogenic, and that the reason for this is that the ocean is not dissolving the atmospheric CO_2 which the chemical laws (cf. Henry's Law) say it should.

Bolin & Eriksson (1959) correctly state: "First we see that if the partial pressure of CO_2 varies and the hydrogen ion concentration were kept constant, the relative changes would be the same in the sea as in the atmosphere. As the total amount of CO_2 in the sea is about 50 times that in the air, practically all excess CO_2 delivered to the atmosphere would be taken up by the sea when equilibrium has been established." They further cite Revelle & Suess (1957) that: "most of the CO_2 due to combustion has been transferred into the ocean and that a net increase of CO_2 in the atmosphere of only a few percent has actually occurred. Callendar's deduction has therefore been rejected". They also accept an atmospheric lifetime of about 5 years. This is all in accordance with the laws of chemistry and the carbon isotope ratios of atmospheric CO_2 (Segalstad, 1996).

Such a situation would not fit the heavily criticized atmospheric CO_2 level rise constructed by Callendar (1958) characterized by Bolin & Eriksson (1959) as: "deduced from a careful survey of all available measurements". Bolin & Eriksson (1959) go on to model an ocean without its primary chemical buffer agent calcium carbonate and without organic matter (as all later carbon cycle modellers also have done). They further cite from the discussion of Revelle & Suess (1957) that the sea could have a 'buffer' factor: "a buffer mechanism acting in such a way that a 10% increase of the CO_2-content of the atmosphere need merely be balanced by an increase of about 1% of the total CO_2 content in sea water to reach a new equilibrium". . . . . "The low buffering capacity of the sea mentioned by Revelle and Suess is due to a change in the dissociation equilibrium between CO_2 and H_2CO_3 on one hand and HCO_3 [-] and CO_3[-2] ions on the other."

They neglect, however, the conclusion from the discussion by Revelle & Suess (1957, page 25): "It seems therefore quite improbable that an increase in the atmospheric CO_2 concentration of as much as 10% could have been caused by industrial fuel combustion during the past century, as Callendar's statistical analyses indicate."

It is appropriate at this point to add that if Bolin & Eriksson's conditions in the last paragraph were true, carbonated beer (Bohren, 1987) and soda pop as we know it would be an impossibility with their buffer factor (see below); rain and fresh water would not show the observed equilibrium pH of 5.7 (Krauskopf, 1979); and experiments would not show complete isotopic equilibrium between CO_2 and water in just hours, which in turn is the prerequisite for routine stable isotope analysis involving CO_2 (Gonfiantini, 1981).

Experimentally it has been found that CO_2 and pure water at 25 °C reaches 99% isotopic equilibrium after 30 hours and 52 minutes; after shaking (like wave agitation) 99% equilibrium is reached after 4 hours and 37 minutes (Gonfiantini, 1981). At 350 ppmv CO_2 in the air, the equilibrium concentration of carbonic acid in pure water will be about 0.00001 molal at 25°C. This chemical equilibrium is reached within 20 seconds (Stumm & Morgan, 1970). At the same temperature, at pH-values between 7 and 9, CO_2 reaches 99% chemical equilibrium with water and calcium carbonate in about 100 seconds (Dreybrodt et al., 1996).

Carbonated beer, soda pop, and champagne are good analogues to the CO_2 distribution between atmosphere and ocean. In both cases they manifest the equilibrium governed by Henry's Law: the partial pressure of CO_2 in the air will be proportional to the concentration of CO_2 dissolved in water. The proportional constant is the Henry's Law Constant, giving us a partition coefficient for CO_2 between air and water of approximately 1:50 (Revelle & Suess, 1957; Skirrow, 1975; Jaworowski et al., 1992 a; Segalstad, 1996). We have all experienced the fact that carbonated drinks contain much more (about 50 times higher concentration) CO_2 than the air under the bottle cap above the carbonated water. This fact is in harsh contradiction to the Bolin & Eriksson's buffer factor claim that the air will contain much more CO_2 than the carbonated water, when trying to increase the partial pressure of CO_2 from the assumed pre-industrial level of 290 ppmv (pressure less than 0.0003 atmospheres) to a pressure of about 3 atmospheres in the CO_2 above the carbonated water in the brewed drink bottle.

Bolin & Eriksson's buffer factor would give about 10 times higher CO_2 concentration in air vs. sea water at about 0.0003 atmospheres CO_2 partial pressure, increasing dramatically to an air/water CO_2 partition coefficient of about 50:1 at a CO_2 partial pressure of about 0.003 atmospheres (10 times the assumed pre-industrial level; Bacastow & Keeling, 1973; see Section 7 below for more on the buffer factor).

From their untenable conditions Bolin & Eriksson state: "It is obvious that an addition of CO_2 to the atmosphere will only slightly change the CO_2 content of the sea but appreciably effect the CO_2 content of the atmosphere... The decisive factor is instead the rate of overturning of the deep sea." From "the fact that the top layers of the ocean only need to absorb a small amount of CO_2 from the atmosphere", and a CO_2 lifetime of 500 years for the deep ocean, Bolin & Eriksson (1959) reach the conclusion that "an increase of the atmosphere's content of CO_2 of about 10% would have occurred in 1954. This value compares very favourably with the value of 10% given by Callendar (1958) as the total increase until 1955 deduced from a careful survey of all available measurements." By over-simplifying the properties of the ocean, the authors were able to construct a non-equilibrium model remote from observed reality and chemical laws, fitting the non-representative data of Callendar (1958).

At this point one should note that the ocean is composed of more than a 75m thick top layer, that it is deep, and contains organics. The residence time of suspended POC (particular organic carbon; carbon pool of about 1000 giga-tonnes; some 130% of the atmospheric carbon pool) in the deep sea is only 5-10 years. This alone would consume all possible man-made CO_2 from the total fossil fuel reservoir (some 7200 giga-tonnes) if burned during the next 300 years, because this covers 6 to 15 turnovers of the upper-ocean pool of POC, based on radiocarbon (carbon-14) studies (Toggweiler, 1990; Druffel & Williams, 1990; see also Jaworowski et al., 1992a). The alleged long lifetime of 500 years for carbon diffusing to the deep ocean is of no relevance to the debate on the fate of anthropogenic CO_2 and the 'greenhouse effect', because POC can sink to the bottom of the ocean in less than a year (Toggweiler, 1990).

7. Boost for the dogma – the evasion buffer factor

Bacastow & Keeling (1973) elaborate further on Bolin & Eriksson's ocean buffer factor, calling it an 'evasion factor' (also called the 'Revelle factor'; Keeling & Bacastow, 1977), because the buffer factor is not related to a buffer in the chemical sense. A real buffer can namely be defined as a reaction system which modifies or controls the value of an intensive (i.e. mass independent) thermodynamic variable (pressure, temperature, concentration, pH, etc.). The carbonate system in the sea will act as a pH buffer, by the presence of a weak acid (H_2CO_3) and a salt of the acid ($CaCO_3$). The concentration of CO_2 (g) in the atmosphere and of Ca^{2+} (aq) in the ocean will in the equilibrium Earth system also be buffered by the presence of $CaCO_3$ at a given temperature (Segalstad, 1996).

Bacastow & Keeling (1973) show their calculated evasion factors for average ocean surface water as a function of "the partial pressure of CO_2 exerted by the ocean surface water, P_m, and the total inorganic carbon in the water", here designated C_{total}, relative to the respective values they assumed for pre-industrial times. The evasion factor is constructed such that: "if industrial CO_2 production continues to increase, however, the evasion factor will rise with P_m according to the relation shown in Fig. 3. At the same time the short-term capacity of the oceans to absorb CO_2 from the atmosphere will diminish" (Bacastow & Keeling, 1973). The evasion buffer factor is defined as

$$[\ (P_m - P_{m,o}\ )\ /\ P_{m,o}\ ]\ /\ [\ (C_{total} - C_{total,o}\ )\ /\ C_{total,o}\ ]$$

at constant sea water alkalinity. $P_{m,o}$ and $C_{total,o}$ are "pre-industrial values" of P_m and C_{total}, respectively (Bacastow & Keeling, 1973). Slightly different definitions are used in various contexts (Kohlmaier, 1979). We clearly see that this evasion buffer factor is ideologically defined from an assumed model (atmospheric anthropogenic CO_2 increase) and an assumed pre-industrial value for the CO_2 level. These assumed pre-industrial values are calculated by an iteration technique (Bacastow, 1981) from so-called 'apparent dissociation constants', established from empirical measurements at sea, but showing considerable variation between different authors (Takahashi et al., 1976). "There continues to be considerable uncertainty as to the magnitude of the gas exchange coefficient in the ocean", says Sarmiento (1991). The ideologically constructed non-linear evasion buffer factor or 'Revelle factor' is later referred to as if it was established as a law of nature: "known from thermodynamic data" (Keeling & Bacastow, 1977); a gross exaggeration, giving a false scientific credibility to the method and the results from carbon cycle modelling using this buffer factor. This is a beautiful example of circular logic in action, when such a construction as the evasion factor is used in all carbon cycle models on which the IPCC base their anthropogenic CO_2-level-rise evidence. Using the evasion buffer factor instead of the chemical Henry's Law will always explain any CO_2 level rise as being anthropogenic, because that very idea was the basis for the construction of the evasion buffer correction factor.

The results of carbon cycle modelling using the evasion buffer factor are shown in Table 1. Some go even further: according to Revelle & Munk (1977), "the atmospheric carbon dioxide content could rise to about 5 times the pre-industrial value in the early part of the twenty-second century", i.e. in slightly more than 100 years from now.

	Pre-industrial content	After 1000 GT		After 6000 GT	
		Content (GT)	% increase	Content (GT)	% increase
Atmosphere	700	840	20	1880	170
Terrestrial system	3000	3110	4	3655	22
Ocean surface layer	1000	1020	2	1115	12
Deep ocean	35000	35730	2	39050	12

Table 1. Carbon contents in giga-tonnes (GT) for a four-reservoir non-linear non-equilibrium model during the assumed initial pre-industrial situation, after the introduction of 1,000 GT carbon, and after the introduction of 6,000 GT carbon in the form of CO_2 to the atmosphere, using an ideological evasion buffer correction factor of about 9. The first introduction corresponds to the total input from fossil fuel up to about the year 2000; the second is roughly equal to the known accessible reserves of fossil carbon. After Rodhe (1992).

In linear systems the fluxes between the reservoirs are linearly related to the reservoir contents, as in chemical equilibrium systems. In non-linear modelling, non-equilibrium complex relations are assumed, as in 'logistical growth' models. The results after introduction of carbon to the atmosphere in Table 1 is from a simplified non-linear (non-chemical-equilibrium) non-steady state carbon cycle model with no calcium carbonate and no sea organics. The ideological evasion buffer correction factor is set at about 9. As a consequence of this factor, a substantial increase in atmospheric CO_2 from the introduction of a certain amount of fossil carbon is mathematically balanced by a small increase in carbon in the sea layers. We see that the non-linear relations introduced in these current carbon cycle models give rise to substantial calculated variations between the reservoirs. The atmospheric reservoir is in such simplified non-realistic models much more perturbed than any of the other reservoirs (Rodhe, 1992). If this mechanism were true, it would be impossible for breweries to put their CO_2 in beer or soda pop.

The non-linear modelling results in Table 1 have been made to explain the apparent rise in atmospheric CO_2 today of 20% (vs. an assumed pre-industrial level) from fossil fuel burning by default, and predict a 170% increase in CO_2 when we have burned all our fossil fuel. The sea would in these models only see a maximum rise in CO_2 of 12%.

Holmén (1992) emphasises that such "box models and box diffusion models have very few degrees of freedom and they must describe physical, chemical, and biological processes very crudely. They are based on empirical relations rather than on first principles."

8. Trouble for the dogma – the CO_2 'missing sink'

The next problem is that the Mauna Loa atmospheric CO_2 level increase only accounts for approximately 50% of the expected increase from looking at the amount of CO_2 formed from production data for the burning of fossil fuels (e.g., Kerr, 1992). This annual discrepancy of some 3 giga-tonnes of carbon is in the literature called the missing sink (analogous to 'the missing link'; Holmén, 1992). When trying to find this missing sink in the biosphere, carbon cycle modelling has shown that deforestation must have contributed a large amount of CO_2 to the atmosphere. So instead of finding the missing sink in the terrestrial biosphere, they find another CO_2 source! This makes the missing sink problem yet more severe.

Trabalka (1985) summarises the status of carbon cycle modelling and its missing sinks (Trabalka et al., 1985) thus: "As a first approximation in the validation of models, it should be possible to compute a balanced global carbon budget for the contemporary period; to date this has not been achievable and the reasons are still uncertain. ... These models produce estimates of past atmospheric CO_2 levels that are inconsistent with the historical atmospheric CO_2 increase. This inconsistency implies that significant errors in projections are possible using current carbon cycle models."

Bolin's (1986) conclusion regarding carbon cycle models is to the contrary: "We understand the basic features of the global carbon cycle quite well. It has been possible to construct quantitative models which can be used as a general guide for the projection of future CO_2 concentrations in the atmosphere as a result of given emission scenarios". This is in high contrast to Holmén (1992), who concludes his book chapter on 'The Global Carbon Cycle' with: "obviously our knowledge of the global cycle of carbon is inadequate to get ends to meet."

A 50% error, i.e. the enormous annual amount of about 3 giga-tonnes of carbon not explained by a model, would normally lead to complete rejection of the model and its hypothesis using the scientific method of natural sciences. Yet the inexplicable 50% error in the IPCC argumentation has not caused governments to question the IPCC model. This fact amply demonstrates the success of the 'scare-them-to-death' principle (Section 2 above).

9. Problems for the dogma – CO_2 residence time

A number of lifetimes and time scales are being used in both scientific and policy context, to describe the behaviour of heat-absorbing gases in the atmosphere. These concepts are very important for the discussion on whether anthropogenic CO_2 will be accumulated in the atmosphere and exert an additional global 'greenhouse effect' warming. If each CO_2 molecule in the atmosphere has a short lifetime, it means that the CO_2 molecules will quickly be removed from the atmosphere and absorbed in another reservoir.

A number of definitions for lifetimes of atmospheric CO_2 have been introduced, like 'residence time', 'transit time', 'response time', 'e-folding time', 'turnover time', 'adjustment time', and more varieties of these (e.g., Rodhe, 1992; O'Neill et al., 1994; Rodhe & Björkström, 1979), to try to explain why atmospheric CO_2 allegedly cannot have the short lifetime of approximately 5 years which numerous measurements of different kinds show. It is said that because we observe the atmospheric CO_2 level increase, which apparently has not been dissolved by the sea, the turnover time of atmospheric CO_2 "of the combined system" must be several hundred years (Rodhe, 1992).

IPCC defines the lifetime of CO_2 as the time required for the atmosphere to adjust to a future equilibrium state if emissions change abruptly, and give a lifetime of 50-200 years in parentheses (Houghton et al., 1990). Their footnote no. 4 to their table 1.1 explains: "For each gas in the table, except CO_2, the 'lifetime' is defined here as the ratio of the atmospheric content to the total rate of removal. This time scale also characterises the rate of adjustment of the atmospheric concentrations if the emission rates are changed abruptly. CO_2 is a special case since it has no real sinks, but is merely circulated between various reservoirs (atmosphere, ocean, biota). The lifetime of CO_2 given in the table is a rough indication of the time it would take for the CO_2 concentration to adjust to changes in the emissions ... ".

O'Neill et al. (1994) criticise the IPCC report (Houghton et al., 1990) because it "offers no rigorous definition of lifetime; for the purpose of defining 'global warming potentials', it instead presents integrations of impulse-response functions over several

199

finite time intervals. Each of these estimates has its own strengths and weaknesses. Taken together, however, they create confusion over what 'lifetime' means, how to calculate it, and how it relates to other time scales." IPCC's assertion that CO_2 has no real sinks, have been rejected elsewhere (Jaworowski et al., 1992a; Segalstad, 1996).

The atmospheric residence time (i.e. lifetime; turnover time) of CO_2 has been quantified according to measurements of natural radiocarbon (carbon-14) levels in the atmosphere and the ocean surface, the changes in these levels caused by anthropogenic effects, like 'bomb carbon-14' added to the atmosphere by nuclear explosions, the 'Suess Effect' caused by the addition of old carbon-14-free CO_2 from combustion of fossil fuels; and the application of gas exchange theory to rates determined for the inert radioactive gas radon-222. The results from these measurements are shown in Table 2, mainly based on the compilation by Sundquist (1985), in addition to the solubility data of Murray (1992), and the carbon-13/carbon-12 mass-balance calculation of Segalstad (1992). Both of the last recent measurements happened to give a lifetime of 5.4 years based on completely different methods.

Judged from the data of Table 2 there is apparently very little disagreement from early works to later works regardless of measurement method, and the atmospheric CO_2 lifetime is quite short, nearer five years. This fact was also acknowledged early by IPCC's chairman Bolin (Bolin & Eriksson, 1959).

We should also note that a large number of the atmospheric CO_2 lifetime measurements are based on anthropogenic additions of CO_2 to the atmosphere by 'bomb carbon-14'. It is important for the understanding of the robustness of the ocean to deal with the anthropogenic extra CO_2 that the measured lifetimes are within the same range as for natural carbon-14 before and after the nuclear bomb tests in the early nineteen-sixties. They are also coincident with lifetimes found when considering anthropogenic CO_2 from human burning of fossil fuel, both from carbon-14 as well as for carbon-13/carbon-12 isotopes. The measured lifetimes in Table 2 therefore represent the real lifetime of atmospheric CO_2 in dynamic contact with all its sources and sinks with 'perturbations' included. Hence other 'lifetimes' found by non-linear carbon cycle modelling are irrelevant.

The short atmospheric CO_2 lifetime of 5 years means that CO_2 is quickly being taken out of the atmospheric reservoir, and

	Authors [publication year]	Residence time (years)
Based on natural carbon-14	Craig [1957]	7 +/- 3
	Revelle & Suess [1957]	7
	Arnold & Anderson [1957]	10
	including living & dead biosphere	
	(Siegenthaler, 1989)	4-9
	Craig [1958]	7 +/- 5
	Bolin & Eriksson [1959]	5
	Broecker [1963]	8
	(recalc. by Broecker & Peng, [1974])	
	Craig [1963]	5-15
	Keeling [1973b]	7
	Broecker [1974]	9.2
	Oeschger et al. [1975]	6-9
	Keeling [1979]	7.53
	Peng et al. [1979]	7.6 (5.5-9.4)
	Siegenthaler et al. [1980]	7.5
	Lal & Suess [1983]	3-25
	Siegenthaler [1983]	7.9-10.6
	Kratz et al. [1983]	6.7
Based on Suess Effect	Ferguson [1958]	2 (1-8)
	Bacastow & Keeling [1973]	6.3-7.0
Based on bomb carbon-14	Bien & Suess [1967]	>10
	Münnich & Roether [1967]	5.4
	Nydal [1968]	5-10
	Young & Fairhall [1968]	4-6
	Rafter & O'Brian [1970]	12
	Machta (1972)	2
	Broecker et al. [1980a]	6.2-8.8
	Stuiver [1980]	6.8
	Quay & Stuiver [1980]	7.5
	Delibrias [1980]	6.0
	Druffel & Suess [1983]	12.5
	Siegenthaler [1983]	6.99-7.54
Based on radon-222	Broecker & Peng [1974]	8
	Peng et al. [1979]	7.8-13.2
	Peng et al. [1983]	8.4
Based on solubility data	Murray (1992)	5.4
Based on carbon-13/carbon-12 mass balance		
	Segalstad (1992)	5.4

Table 2. Atmospheric residence time (= lifetime, turnover time) of CO_2, mainly based on the compilation by Sundquist (1985; for references in brackets).

that approximately 135 giga-tonnes (about 18%) of the atmospheric CO_2 pool is exchanged each year. This large and fast natural CO_2 cycling flux is far more than the approximately 6 giga-tonnes of carbon in the anthropogenic fossil fuel CO_2 now contributed annually to the atmosphere, which creates so much political turmoil (Segalstad, 1992; 1996).

IPCC supporters have apparently not been satisfied with these facts based on numerous measurements and methods. They go on by saying that because we observe the atmospheric CO_2 level increase, it must be caused by Man's burning of fossil fuel, and the lifetime of atmospheric CO_2 must be 50-200 years (Houghton et al., 1990). Hence, they say, when we construct non-linear (non-proportional and non-chemical-equilibrium) non-steady-state systems for the fluxes between the ocean surface layer, the atmosphere, and the terrestrial system, the decay time of man-made carbon into the atmosphere must be much longer than the turn-over time (Rodhe & Björkström, 1979). If we now use a constructed evasion buffer factor (Section 5 and 6 above) of 10, the atmospheric CO_2 lifetime will be 10 times the measured (real) lifetime of 5 years, namely 50 years or more (Rodhe & Björkström, 1979; Rodhe, 1992).

To rephrase: an apparent atmospheric CO_2 level rise, assumed to be due to human burning of fossil fuel, is being treated with non-linear (non-proportional and non-chemical-equilibrium) non-steady-state modelling, giving theoretical lifetimes far longer than those actually measured. When this is not explained to the readers, they are led astray, gaining the impression that the artificial assumed model lifetimes are real lifetimes. In fact there is no consistent definition of residence time by the IPCC.

Or as O'Neill et al. (1994) phrase it: "A growing array of time scales are being extracted from carbon cycle models and data and their relationships have not been clear. ... This discrepancy has not been adequately explained and is causing confusion in the literature concerned with the atmospheric lifetime of anthropogenic CO_2 ... Considering the policy implications of such numbers, it is important that their meanings and relationships be fully clarified."

Rodhe & Björkström (1979) conclude their treatment of carbon cycle and CO_2 lifetime modelling by saying: "Naturally, we do not claim that such very simplified models of the carbon cycle, which we have studied, contain the final answer to the very complex question of how nature will distribute the man-made CO_2 emissions between the major reservoirs. That question should be studied with the aid of much more sophisticated models which take into account more of our knowledge about the physical and chemical processes involved."

10. The breakdown of the dogma – carbon isotopes

Suess (1955) estimated for 1953, based on the carbon-14 'Suess Effect' (dilution of the atmospheric CO_2 with CO_2 from burning of fossil fuel, devoid of carbon-14), arguing "that the world-wide contamination of the Earth's atmosphere with artificial CO_2 probably amounts to less than 1%". Revelle & Suess (1957) calculated on the basis of new carbon-14 data that the amount of atmospheric "CO_2 derived from industrial fuel combustion" would be 1.73% for an atmospheric CO_2 lifetime of 7 years, and 1.2% for a CO_2 lifetime of 5 years.

The IPCC assumed that CO_2 has risen by 21% since the industrial revolution due to the burning of fossil fuels. (IPCC, 1990). This conflicts with the above analysis.

Such a large contradiction between the carbon-14 measurements and the IPCC position, has worried many researchers. In order to make Suess' measurements fit the dogma, it would be necessary to mix the atmospheric fossil-fuel CO_2 with CO_2 from a different carbon reservoir five times larger than the atmosphere alone (Broecker et al., 1979). It was alternatively proposed that the carbon-14-labelled CO_2 would act completely differently than the 'ordinary' CO_2: "However, the system's responses are not the same for the CO_2 concentration and for isotopic ratios" (Oeschger & Siegenthaler, 1978). The explanation given is that the CO_2 levels will be governed by the constructed evasion buffer correction factor, while on the other hand (strangely enough) the isotope ratios of the atoms in the very same CO_2 molecules would be unaffected by the evasion buffer factor, and furthern, "would be equal in both reservoirs [the atmosphere and the ocean's mixed layer] at equilibrium. This explains why the relative atmospheric CO_2 increase is larger than the Suess effect" (Oeschger & Siegenthaler, 1978). This cannot be accepted, when all chemical and isotopic experiments indicate that equilibrium between CO_2 and water is obtained within a few hours (see Section 5 above).

Ratios between the carbon-13 and carbon-12 stable isotopes are commonly expressed in permil by a so-called delta-13-C notation being the standard-normalised difference from the standard, multiplied by 1000. The international standard for stable carbon isotopes is the Pee Dee Belemnite (PDB) calcium carbonate.

CO_2 from combustion of fossil fuel and from biospheric materials have delta-13-C values near -26 permil. 'Natural' CO_2 has delta-13-C values of -7 permil in equilibrium with CO_2 dissolved in the hydrosphere and in marine calcium carbonate. Mixing these two atmospheric CO_2 components: IPCC's 21% CO_2 from fossil fuel burning + 79% 'natural' CO_2 should give a delta-13-C of the present atmospheric CO_2 of approximately -11 permil, calculated by isotopic mass balance (Segalstad, 1992; 1996).

This atmospheric CO_2 delta-13-C mixing value of -11 permil to be expected from IPCC's model is not found in actual measurements. Keeling et al. (1989) reported a measured atmospheric delta-13-C value of -7.489 permil in December 1978, decreasing to -7.807 permil in December 1988 (the significance of all their digits not justified). These values are close to the value of the natural atmospheric CO_2 reservoir, far from the delta-13-C value of -11 permil expected from the IPCC model.

From the measured delta-13-C values in atmospheric CO_2 we can by isotopic mass balance also calculate that the amount of fossil-fuel CO_2 in the atmosphere is equal to or less than 4%, supporting the carbon-14 'Suess Effect' evidence. Hence the IPCC model is neither supported by radioactive nor stable carbon isotope evidence (Segalstad, 1992; 1993; 1996).

To explain this apparent contradiction versus the IPCC model, the observed delta-13-C value of atmospheric CO_2 "must be affected by other heavier [i.e. with high delta-13-C values] carbon sources, such as is derived from the air-sea exchange process" (Inoue & Sugimura, 1985). One way to make this happen, would be if the isotopic exchange from air to sea were different from the isotopic exchange from sea to air, i.e. a gross non-equilibrium situation would be required. Siegenthaler & Münnich (1981) were able to construct such a simple theoretical kinetic, non-equilibrium model: "Diffusion of CO_2 into the water, which is rate limiting for mean oceanic conditions, fractionates the carbon isotopes only little. 13-C/12-C fractionations are found to be -1.8 to -2.3 permil for atmosphere-to-ocean transfer, and -9.7 to -10.2 permil for ocean-to-atmosphere transfer."

Inoue & Sugimura (1985) attempted to verify these kinetic isotope fractionations experimentally at three temperatures: 288.2; 296.2; and 303.2 Kelvin, versus their equilibrium values of -8.78; -7.86; and -7.10 permil, respectively, all with uncertainty given as +/- 0.05 permil. Their reported air to sea fractionations at these temperatures were -2 +/- 3; -4 +/- 5; and -5 +/- 7 permil, respectively. Their sea to air fractionations were found to be -10 +/- 4; -13 +/- 6; and -12 +/- 7 permil, respectively. (Reported alpha fractionation factors and uncertainties have here been recalculated to alpha minus one, multiplied by 1000, to get comparable fractionation values). They conclude that the agreement is fairly good with the theoretically deduced values of Siegenthaler & Münnich (1981). Looking at the reported uncertainties, however, the experimental data cannot be grouped in three populations; their air-to-sea and sea-to-air data are not significantly different from their reported air/sea/air equilibrium value at the three different temperatures. Hence the experimental data cannot be used as evidence for the proposed theoretical difference in isotopic fractionation for air/sea versus sea/air CO_2 transfer due to differences in kinetic isotope fractionation.

Siegenthaler & Oeschger (1987), in their carbon cycle modelling, with carbon isotopes included, touch on the possibility that the apparent atmospheric CO_2 level increase is due to marine degassing instead of accumulation of anthropogenic CO_2: "We will also discuss the sensitivity of the model results to uncertainties in the ice core data, to different model assumptions and to the (unlikely) possibility that the non-fossil CO_2 was not of biospheric, but rather of marine origin." The word 'unlikely' in parentheses is indeed their wording. Their modelling shows, ambiguously, that: "as expected, the results are similar to those for the fossil-only input." But their modelling shows a discrepancy with the ice core CO_2 data, in addition to: "it is somewhat surprising that observations and model agree for 13-C but not for 14-C; this can, however, not be discussed here any further". In their abstract, however, they conclude on the contrary: "Calculated 13-C and 14-C time histories agree well with the observed changes."

The carbon cycle modelling of Siegenthaler & Oeschger (1987) run into several problems making their models fit all the data, leading them to write: "One possibility is that the assumptions underlying our results are not fully correct, i.e., that either the Siple ice core data deviate from the true atmospheric concentration history or that the carbon cycle models used do not yield the correct fluxes. If we dismiss these possibilities, then other carbon sinks than the ocean seem to exist." For the lack of validity of the Siple ice core, see Section 4 above.

Based on this kind of modelling, IPCC states as part of their "evidence that the contemporary carbon dioxide increase is anthropogenic" (their Section 1.2.5; Houghton, 1990): "Third, the observed isotopic trends of 13-C and 14-C agree qualitatively with those expected due to the CO_2 emissions from fossil fuels and the biosphere, and they are quantitatively consistent with the results from carbon cycle modelling." Such a correspondence is, however, not evident to the present author.

Segalstad (1992; 1993; 1996) concluded from 13-C/12-C isotope mass balance calculations, in accordance with the 14-C data, that at least 96% of the current atmospheric CO_2 is isotopically indistinguishable from non-fossil-fuel sources, i.e. natural marine and juvenile sources from the Earth's interior. Hence, for the atmospheric CO_2 budget, marine equilibration and degassing, and juvenile degassing from e.g. volcanic sources, must be much more important, and the sum of burning of fossil-fuel and biogenic releases (4%) much less important, than is assumed (21% of atmospheric CO_2) by the authors of the IPCC model (Houghton et al., 1990).

The apparent annual atmospheric CO_2 level increase, postulated to be anthropogenic, would constitute only some 0.2% of the total annual amount of CO_2 exchanged naturally between the atmosphere and the ocean plus other natural sources and sinks (Section 9 above). It is more probable that such a small ripple in the annual natural flow of CO_2 is caused by natural fluctuations of geophysical processes. We have no database for disproving this judgement (Trabalka, 1985). As Brewer (1983) puts it: "Nature has vast resources with which to fool us . . .".

Segalstad's mass balance calculations show that IPCC's atmospheric CO_2 lifetime of 50-200 years would make the atmosphere too light (50% of its current CO_2 mass) to fit its measured 13-C/12-C ratio. This shows why IPCC's incorrect model creates its artificial 50% missing sink (Segalstad, 1996).

11. Conclusion

The atmospheric CO_2 level is ultimately determined by geologic processes. The carbon on the Earth's surface has come from CO_2 degassing of the Earth's interior, which has released about half of its estimated CO_2 contents throughout Earth's history during the 4,500 million years up to now (Holland, 1984). Important geologic processes are volcanism and erosion, releasing carbon from the lithosphere and the Earth's interior to the atmosphere–ocean–biosphere system. These processes are counteracted by sedimentation of carbonate and organic carbon in the hydrosphere (mainly the ocean). The balance between these two main processes determines the CO_2 level in the atmosphere (e.g., Kramer, 1965; McDuff & Morel, 1980; Walker & Drever, 1988; Holmén, 1992). "Thus, while seawater alkalinity is directly controlled by the formation of calcium carbonate as its major sedimentary sink, it is also controlled indirectly by carbonate metamorphism which buffers the CO_2 content of the atmosphere" (McDuff & Morel, 1980).

In addition there is a short-term carbon cycle dominated by an exchange of CO_2 between the atmosphere and biosphere through photosynthesis, respiration, and putrefaction (decay), and similarly between aqueous CO_2 (including its products of hydrolysis and protolysis) and marine organic matter (Walker & Drever, 1988).

Analogously to the transfer of anthropogenic CO_2 to the atmosphere, it seems appropriate to cite Walker (1994): "Consider, now some perturbation of the system – for example, the doomsday perturbation that suddenly stops photosynthesis. In 20 years or so, all the carbon in the biota reservoir will be released to the atmosphere, leading initially to a large increase in the amount of carbon dioxide in the atmosphere. But in no time at all, in terms of human generations, that extra carbon dioxide will work its way down into the very deep sea reservoir where the addition of 2×10^{17} moles to the 30×10^{17} moles already there will have little effect. The system will not end up with a lot of extra carbon dioxide in the atmosphere, even if photosynthesis stops completely. The figure shows also the fossil fuel rate, which is smaller than the rate of photosynthesis."

It is nature's coupling between the temporary, short-lived atmospheric reservoir, with 0.5×10^{17} moles CO_2, and the relatively enormous oceanic reservoir, with 30×10^{17} moles of dissolved (and hydrolyzed and protolyzed) CO_2 in contact with calcium carbonate, that determines the amount of CO_2 in the atmosphere. This coupling is in turn coupled to the much larger lithospheric reservoir. The rates and fluxes of the latter coupling control the amount of carbon in the surface reservoir of the Earth. All kinds of measurements show that the real residence time of atmospheric CO_2 is about 5 years.

Chemical and isotope equilibrium considerations and the short CO_2 residence time (lifetime) can fully explain the carbon cycle of the Earth. The conclusion of such reasoning is that any atmospheric CO_2 level rise beyond 4% cannot be explained by accumulation of CO_2 from Man's burning of fossil fuel. An apparent CO_2 rise can only come from a much larger, but natural, carbon reservoir with much higher delta-13-C than the fossil fuel pool, namely from the ocean, and/or the lithosphere, and/or the Earth's interior. CO_2 degassing from the oceans instead of IPCC's anthropogenic atmospheric accumulation is indeed made probable by the measurements of a larger CO_2 increase in Atlantic surface waters than in the contemporaneous atmosphere (Takahashi, 1961; 1979). Kondratyev (1988) argues that: "The fact is that the atmospheric CO_2 content may be controlled by the climate" and not the opposite.

Trabalka (1985) concluded: "The available data on past fluctuations in atmospheric CO_2 and climate suggest that our current carbon cycle models, which emphasize human perturbations, may be missing natural feedback components involving both terrestrial and marine systems, perhaps even climate-induced 'mode switches' in ocean circulation patterns, which could be very important in understanding changes in both climate and the carbon cycle over the next century."

Such conclusions will not make the large 'doomsday' headlines in the news media, will not enable politicians to implement extra taxes or legislation, will not justify expensive conferences organized by the United Nations or other international bodies, will not allow environmental organisations to preach about human wickedness, and will not bring any research support money from governments or research foundations.

IPCC (Houghton et al., 1990) claims in their Section 1.2.5 three evidences that the contemporary atmospheric CO_2 increase is anthropogenic: (1) CO_2 measurements from ice cores show a 21% rise from 280 to 353 ppmv since pre-industrial times; (2) the atmospheric CO_2 increase closely parallels the accumulated emission trends from fossil fuel combustion and from land use changes, although the annual increase has been smaller each year than the fossil CO_2 input [some 50% deviation, e.g. Kerr, 1992]; (3) the observed isotopic trends of 13-C and 14-C agree qualitatively with those expected due to the CO_2 emissions from fossil fuels and the biosphere, and they are quantitatively consistent with results from carbon cycle modelling.

Jaworowski et al. (1992 a, 1992 b) reviewed published CO_2 measurements from ice cores, and rejected this method because it cannot give reliable data for either the CO_2 level history of paleoatmospheres or the pre-industrial atmospheric CO_2 level. The paper by Jaworowski et al. (1992 a) and this paper have addressed recent atmospheric CO_2 measurements by a non-validated instrumental method with results visually selected and 'edited', deviating from unselected measurements of constant CO_2 levels by the highly accurate wet-chemical technique at 19 stations in Northern Europe (Bischof, 1960). Hence a rise in global atmospheric CO_2 level has not yet been significantly justified by validated methods and sound statistics. Stable carbon isotope mass balance calculations based on 13-C/12-C measurements prove why IPCC's wrong model creates their inexplicable 50% missing sink (Segalstad, 1996).

Carbon isotopic trends agree *qualitatively* with fossil fuel CO_2 emissions like stated by IPCC, but show *quantitatively* a fossil fuel CO_2 component of a maximum of 4% versus the 21% claimed by IPCC. This paper has further examined and rejected the carbon cycle modelling forming the basis for IPCC evidence. It is shown that carbon cycle modelling based on non-equilibrium models, remote from observed reality and chemical laws, made to fit non-representative data through the use of non-linear correction buffer factors constructed from a pre-conceived hypothesis, constitute a circular argument having no scientific validity. IPCC's non-realistic carbon cycle modelling will simply refute reality, like the existence of carbonated beer or soda pop as we know it.

The CO_2 dogma is based on the hypothesis that the release of CO_2 from fossil fuel burning will cause this extra atmospheric CO_2 to increase the temperature of the lower atmosphere. It is important to note that due to the atmosphere's extremely low heat capacity, the heat energy accumulated in the atmosphere from this process will be minute and unable to change the Earth's climate. This, compared with the enormous heat energy stored in the oceans, and the enormous heat energy required to melt the cryosphere (ice sheets, sea ice, permafrost, and glaciers), is insignificant. It would be impossible to melt the Earth's ice caps and thereby increase the sea level just by increasing the heat energy of the atmosphere through a few percent of added heat absorbing anthropogenic CO_2 in the lower atmosphere (Segalstad, 1996). Furthermore, there exists no proof of a constantly rising trend for the temperature of the world's lower atmosphere since the industrial revolution (e.g., Jaworowski et al., 1992a; Michaels & Knappenberger, 1996).

A dogma is, according to dictionaries, considered an arrogant and authoritative declaration of opinion based on a priori principles, not on induction, and often as a sacrament or commandment for religious belief. Review of the basis for the CO_2 dogma makes its components appear neither supported by reality nor the scientific method of natural sciences, making it rather a preconceived idea or tenet sharing most features of a dogma.

Acknowledgements

Drs. H. M. Seip and J. S. Fuglestvedt at 'Cicero' (the Norwegian government constituted institute for climate politics) are acknowledged for discussions leading to the strengthening and clarification of the conclusions of this paper.

References

Arrhenius, S. (1896): On the influence of carbonic acid in the air upon the temperature of the ground. *London, Edinburgh, Dublin Philos. Mag. J. Sci., Ser. 5, 41,* 237-276.

Bacastow, R. (1981): Numerical evaluation of the evasion factor. *In:* Bolin, B. (Ed.): *Carbon cycle modelling (SCOPE 16).* John Wiley & Sons, 95-101.

Bacastow, R. & Keeling, C.D. (1973): Atmospheric carbon dioxide and radiocarbon in the natural carbon cycle: II. Changes from A.D. 1700 to 2070 as deduced from a geochemical model. *In:* Woodwell, G.M. & Pecan, E.V. (Eds.): *Carbon and the biosphere.* CONF-72051. Technical Information Center, Office of Information Services, United States Atomic Energy Commission, 86-135.

Bacastow, R., Keeling, C.D. & Whorp, T.P. (1985): Seasonal amplitude increase in atmospheric CO_2 concentration at Mauna Loa, Hawaii, 1959-1982. *Journal of Geophysical Research 90,* 10529-10540.

Barnola, J.M., Raynaud, D., Korotkevich, Y. S. & Lorius, C. (1987): Vostok ice core provides 160,000-year record of atmospheric CO_2. *Nature 329,* 408-414.

Bischof, W. (1960): Periodical variations of the atmospheric CO_2-content in Scandinavia. *Tellus 12,* 216-226.

Bohren, C.F. (1987): *Clouds in a glass of beer: simple experiments in atmospheric physics.* Wiley Science Editions, John Wiley & Sons, Inc., 195 pp.

Bolin, B. (1986): How much CO_2 will remain in the atmosphere? *In:* Bolin, B., Döös, B. R., Jäger, J. & Warrick, R. A. (Eds.): *The Greenhouse Effect, climatic change, and ecosystems (SCOPE 29).* John Wiley & Sons, 93-155.

Bolin, B. & Eriksson, E. (1959): Changes in the carbon dioxide content of the atmosphere and sea due to fossil fuel combustion. *In:* Bolin, B. (Ed.): *The atmosphere and the sea in motion. Scientific contributions to the Rossby Memorial Volume.* The Rockefeller Institute Press, New York, 130-142.

Böttcher, F. (1996): Climate change: forcing a treaty. In: ESEF *The Global Warming Debate. The report of the European Science and Environment Forum.* Cambridge, 267-285.

Bray, J. R. (1959): An analysis of the possible recent change in atmospheric carbon dioxide concentration. *Tellus 11,* 220-230.

Brewer, P. G. (1983): Past and future atmospheric concentrations of carbon dioxide; carbon dioxide and the oceans. *In: Changing climate.* National Academy Press, 188-215.

Broecker, W. S., Takahashi, T., Simpson, H.J. & Peng, T.-H. (1979): Fate of fossil fuel carbon dioxide and the global carbon budget. *Science 206,* 409-418.

Callendar, G. S. (1938): The artificial production of carbon dioxide and its influence on temperature. *Quarterly Journal of the Royal Meteorological Society 64,* 223-240.

Callendar, G. S. (1940): Variations of the amount of carbon dioxide in different air currents. *Quarterly Journal of the Royal Meteorological Society 66,* 395-400.

Callendar, G. S. (1949): Can carbon dioxide influence climate? *Weather 4,* 310-314.

Callendar, G. S. (1958): On the amount of carbon dioxide in the atmosphere. *Tellus 10,* 243-248.

Churchman, C.W. (1948): *Theory of experimental inference.* Macmillan, New York, 292 pp.

Cialdini, R.B. (1993): *Influence: the psychology of persuasion, 2nd. rev. ed.* William Morrow & Co., Inc., New York, 320 pp.

Craig, H. (1957): The natural distribution of radio carbon and the exchange time of carbon dioxide between the atmosphere and sea. *Tellus 9,* 1-16.

Dreybrodt, W., Lauckner, J., Zaihua, L., Svensson, U. & Buhmann, D. (1996): The kinetics of the reaction $CO_2 + H_2O \rightarrow H^+ + HCO_3^-$ as one of the rate limiting steps for the dissolution of calcite in the system $H_2O - CO_2 - CaCO_3$. *Geochimica et Cosmochimica Acta 60,* 3375-3381.

Druffel, E.R.M. & Williams, P.M. (1990): Identification of a deep marine source of particulate organic carbon using bomb carbon-14. *Nature 347,* 172-174.

Etheridge, D. M., Pearman, G. I. & de Silva, F. (1988): Atmospheric trace-gas variations as revealed by air trapped in an ice core from Law Dome, Antarctica. *Annals of Glaciology 10*, 28-33.

Fonselius, S., Koroleff, F. & Warme, K.-E. (1956): Carbon dioxide in the atmosphere. *Tellus 8*, 176-183.

Gonfiantini, R. (1981): The delta-notation and the mass-spectrometric measurement techniques. *International Atomic Agency, Technical Report Series 210*, 35-84.

Holland, H. (1984): *The chemical evolution of the atmosphere and oceans.* Princeton University Press, 582 pp.

Holmén, K. (1992): The global carbon cycle. *In:* Butcher, S. S., Charlson, R.J., Orians, G.H. & Wolfe, G.V. (Eds.): *Global biogeochemical cycles.* Academic Press, 239-262.

Inoue, H. & Sugimura, Y. (1985): Carbon isotopic fractionation during the CO_2 exchange process between air and sea water under equilibrium and kinetic conditions. *Geochimica et Cosmochimica Acta 49*, 2453-2460.

IPCC (1990). Houghton, J.T., Jenkins, G.J. & Ephraums, J.J. (eds.): *Climate Change. The IPCC Scientific Assessment. Intergovernmental Panel on Climate Change.* Cambridge University Press, Cambridge, 365 pp.

Jaworowski, Z., Segalstad, T.V. & Hisdal, V. (1992 a): Atmospheric CO_2 and global warming: a critical review; 2nd revised edition. *Norsk Polarinstitutt, Meddelelser [Norwegian Polar Institute, Memoirs] 119*, 76 pp.

Jaworowski, Z., Segalstad, T.V. & Ono, N. (1992 b): Do glaciers tell a true atmospheric CO_2 story? *Science of the Total Environment 114*, 227-284.

Keeling, C.D. & Bacastow, R.B. (1977): Impact of industrial gases on climate. *In: Energy & Climate.* Studies in Geophysics, National Academy of Sciences, Washington, DC, 72-95.

Keeling, C.D., Bacastow, R.B., Carter, A. F., Piper, S.C., Whorf, T.P., Heimann, M., Mook, W.G. & Roeloffzen, H. (1989): A three-dimensional model of atmospheric CO_2 transport based on observed winds: 1. Analysis of observational data. *In:* Peterson, D. H. (Ed.): Aspects of climate variability in the Pacific and the

Western Americas. *American Geophysical Union, Geophysical Monograph 55,* 165-236.

Kerr, R. A. (1992): Fugitive carbon dioxide: it's not hiding in the ocean. *Science 256,* 35.

Kohlmaier, G.H. (1979): Dynamics of the surface ocean – deep see carbon exchange in its relation to the atmosphere – surface ocean exchange. *In:* Bolin, B. (Ed.): *Carbon cycle modelling (SCOPE 16).* John Wiley & Sons, 307-314.

Kondratyev, K.Y. (1988): *Climate shocks: natural and anthropogenic.* John Wiley & Sons, 296 pp.

Kramer, J. R. (1965): History of sea water. Constant temperature-pressure equilibrium models compared to liquid inclusion analyses. *Geochimica et Cosmochimica Acta 29,* 92-945.

Krauskopf, K. B. (1979): *Introduction to geochemistry, 2nd. ed.* McGraw-Hill, 617 pp.

Machta, L. (1972): The role of the oceans and the biosphere in the carbon dioxide cycle. In Dryssen, D. & Jagner, D. (eds.): *The changing chemistry of the oceans. Nobel Symposium 20.* Almquist & Wiksell/Wiley Interscience, New York, 121-145.

McDuff, R.E. & Morel, F.M.M. (1980): The geochemical control of seawater (Sillen revisited). *Environmental Science & Technology 14,* 1182-1186.

McKay, CP., Toon, O.B. & Kasting, J.F. (1991): Making Mars habitable. *Nature 352,* 489-496.

Michaels, P.J. & Knappenberger, P.C. (1996): The United Nations Intergovernmental Panel on Climate Change and the scientific 'consensus' on global warming. *In:* Emsley, J. (Ed.): *The Global Warming Debate. The report of the European Science and Environment Forum.* Cambridge: European Science and Environment Forum, 158-178.

Murray, J.W. (1992): The oceans. *In:* Butcher, S. S., Charlson, R.J., Orians, G.H. & Wolfe, G.V. (Eds.): *Global biogeochemical cycles.* Academic Press, 175-211.

Næss, A. (1990): *Ecology, community and lifestyle.* Cambridge University Press, Cambridge, 223 pp.

Neftel, A., Moor, E., Oeschger, H. & Stauffer, B. (1985): Evidence from polar ice cores for the increase in atmospheric CO_2 in the past two centuries. *Nature 315,* 45-47.

Neftel, A., Oeschger, H., Schwander, J., Stauffer, B. & Zumbrunn, R. (1982): Ice core sample measurements give atmospheric CO_2 content during the past 40,000 years. *Nature 295,* 220-223.

Neftel, A., Oeschger, H., Staffelbach, T. & Stauffer, B. (1988): CO_2 record in the Byrd ice core 50,000 – 5,000 years BP. *Nature 331,* 609 – 611.

Oeschger, H. & Siegenthaler, U. (1978): The dynamics of the carbon cycle as revealed by isotope studies. *In:* Williams, J. (Ed.): *Carbon dioxide, climate and society.* Pergamon Press, 45-61.

Oeschger, H., Stauffer, B., Finkel, R. & Langway, C.C., Jr. (1985): Variations of the CO_2 concentration of occluded air and of anions and dust in polar ice cores. *In:* Sundquist, E. T. & Broecker, W. S. (Eds.): The carbon cycle and atmospheric CO_2: natural variations Archean to present. *American Geophysical Union, Geophysical Monograph 32,* 132-142.

O'Neill, B. C., Gaffin, S. R., Tubiello, F. N. & Oppenheimer, M. (1994): Reservoir time scales for anthropogenic CO_2 in the atmosphere. *Tellus 46 B,* 378-389.

Pales, J.C. & Keeling, C.D. (1965): The concentration of atmospheric carbon dioxide in Hawaii. *Journal of Geophysical Research 70,* 6053-6076.

Revelle, R. & Munk, W. (1977): The carbon dioxide cycle and the biosphere. *In: Energy & Climate.* Studies in Geophysics, National Academy of Sciences, Washington, DC, 140-158.

Revelle, R. & Suess, H. (1957): Carbon dioxide exchange between atmosphere and ocean and the question of an increase of atmospheric CO_2 during past decades. *Tellus 9,* 18-27.

Rodhe, H. (1992): Modelling biogeochemical cycles. *In:* Butcher, S. S., Charlson, R.J., Orians, G.H. & Wolfe, G.V. (Eds.): *Global biogeochemical cycles.* Academic Press, 55-72.

Rodhe, H. & Björkström, A. (1979): Some consequences of non-proportionality between fluxes and reservoir contents in natural systems. *Tellus 31,* 269-278.

Ryan, S. (1995): Quiescent outgassing of Mauna Loa Volcano 1958-1994. *In:* Rhodes, J.M. & Lockwood, J.P. (Eds.): Mauna Loa revealed: structure, composition, history, and hazards. *American Geophysical Union, Geophysical Monograph 92,* 95-115.

Sanford, R.F. (1992): Environmentalism and the assault on reason. *In:* Lehr, J. (Ed.): *Rational readings on environmental concerns.* Van Nostrand Reinhold, New York, 16-31.

Sarmiento, J.L. (1991): Oceanic uptake of anthropogenic CO_2: the major uncertainties. *Global Biogeochemical Cycles 5,* 309-313.

Segalstad, T.V. (1992): The amount of non-fossil-fuel CO_2 in the atmosphere. *American Geophysical Union, Chapman Conference on Climate, Volcanism, and Global Change, March 23-27, 1992, Hilo, Hawaii. Abstracts,* 25.

Segalstad, T.V. (1993): Stable isotope geochemistry applied to paleoclimatological and greenhouse gas problems. *1st International Symposium on Applied Isotope Geochemistry (AIG-1), Aug. 29 – Sept. 3, 1993, Geiranger, Norway. Program and Abstracts, Institute for Energy Research IFE/KR/E-93/007,* 95-96.

Segalstad, T.V. (1996): The distribution of CO_2 between atmosphere, hydrosphere, and lithosphere; minimal influence from anthropogenic CO_2 on the global 'Greenhouse Effect'. *In:* Emsley, J. (Ed.): *The Global Warming Debate. The report of the European Science and Environment Forum.* Bourne Press, Ltd., Bournemouth, Dorset, UK, 41-50.

Siegenthaler, U. (1989): Carbon-14 in the oceans. *In:* Fritz, P. & Fontes, J.C. (Eds.): *Handbook of environmental isotope geochemistry, 3 A.* Elsevier, 75-136.

Siegenthaler, U. & Münnich, K. O. (1981): 13-C/12-C fractionation during CO_2 transfer from air to sea. *In:* Bolin, B. (Ed.): *Carbon cycle modelling (SCOPE 16).* John Wiley & Sons, 249-257.

Siegenthaler, U. & Oeschger, H. (1987): Biospheric CO_2 emissions during the past 200 years reconstructed by deconvolution of ice core data. *Tellus 39 B,* 140 – 154.

Skirrow, G. (1975): The dissolved gases – carbon dioxide. *In* Riley, J.P. & Skirrow, G. (Eds.): *Chemical oceanography, Vol. 2; 2nd edition.* Academic Press, 1-192.

Slocum, G. (1955): Has the amount of carbon dioxide in the atmosphere changed significantly since the beginning of the twentieth century? *Monthly Weather Review, October,* 225-231.

Stumm, W. & Morgan, J.J. (1970): *Aquatic chemistry: an introduction emphasizing chemical equilibria in natural waters.* Wiley-Interscience, 583 pp.

Suess, H. E. (1955): Radiocarbon concentration in modern wood. *Science 122,* 415-417.

Sundquist, E. T. (1985): Geological perspectives on carbon dioxide and the carbon cycle. *In:* Sundquist, E. T. & Broecker, W. S. (Eds.): The carbon cycle and atmospheric CO_2: natural variations Archean to present. *American Geophysical Union, Geophysical Monograph 32,* 5-59.

Takahashi, T. (1961): CO_2 in the atmosphere and in Atlantic ocean water. *Journal of Geophysical Research 66,* 477-494.

Takahashi, T. (1979): Carbon dioxide chemistry in ocean water. *In:* Elliott, W. P. & Machta, L. (Eds.): *Carbon dioxide effects research and assessment program: workshop on the global effects of carbon dioxide from fossil fuels.* NTIS, U.S. Department of Commerce, 63-71.

Takahashi, T., Kaiteris, P., Broecker, W. S. & Bainbridge, A. E. (1976): An evaluation of the apparent dissociation constants of carbonic acid in seawater. *Earth and Planetary Science Letters 32,* 458-467.

Toggweiler, J. R. (1990): Bombs and ocean carbon cycles. *Nature 347,* 122-123.

Trabalka, J. R. (Ed.) (1985): Executive summary. *Atmospheric carbon dioxide and the global carbon cycle.* United States Department of Energy, DOE/ER-0239, xv-xxiii.

Trabalka, J. R., Edmonds, J.A., Reilly, J., Gardner, R.H. & Voorhees, L.D. (1985): Human alterations of the global carbon cycle and the projected future. *In:* Trabalka, J. R. (Ed.): *Atmospheric carbon dioxide and the global carbon cycle.* United States Department of Energy, DOE/ER-0239, 247-287.

Walker, J.C.G. (1994): Global geochemical cycles of carbon. *In:* Tolbert, N. E. & Preiss, J. (Eds.): *Regulation of atmospheric CO_2 and O_2 by photosynthetic carbon metabolism.* Oxford, 75-89.

Walker, J.C.G. & Drever, J.I. (1988): Geochemical cycles of atmospheric gases. *In:* Gregor, C.B., Garrels, R.M., Mackenzie, F. T. & Maynard, J.B. (Eds.): *Chemical cycles in the evolution of the Earth.* John Wiley & Sons, Ltd., 55-76.

217

Tom Victor Segalstad

Born in Norway in 1949. HoldsUniversity degrees (natural sciences with geology) from the University of Oslo. Has conducted university research, publishing, and teaching in geochemistry, mineralogy, petrology, volcanology, structural geology, ore geology, and geophysics at the University of Oslo, Norway, and the Pennsylvania State University, USA. Is the incumbent Associate Professor of Geochemistry at the University of Oslo, with responsibility for stable isotope geochemistry. He is a past head of the Mineralogical-Geological Museum at the University of Oslo; and past Director of the Natural History Museums and Botanical Garden of the University of Oslo. He is a member of several international and national professional working groups and committees.

Printing errors in the ESEF Vol. 1 paper:

Segalstad, T.V. (1996): The distribution of CO_2 between atmosphere, hydrosphere, and lithosphere; minimal influence from anthropogenic CO_2 on the global 'Greenhouse Effect'. *In:* Emsley, J. (ed.): *The Global Warming Debate. The report of the European Science and Environment Forum:* 41-50.

Page 45, line 4 should read: controls the value of an intensive (= mass independent) thermodynamic variable (pressure,

Page 45, 7th last line should read: and a calcium silicate + CO_2 <-> calcium carbonate + SiO_2 buffer

Page 45, 5th and 4th last lines should read: 'security net' underlying the most important buffer: CO_2 (g) <-> HCO_3^- (aq) <-> $CaCO_3$ (s). All together these buffers, in principle, add

Page 46: all Greek sigmas should read Greek deltas.

Page 46, footnote should read:

1

$$\text{delta}^{13}C \ = \ \frac{(^{13}C/^{12}C)_{\text{sample}} - (^{13}C/^{12}C)_{\text{standard}}}{(^{13}C/^{12}C)_{\text{standard}}} \cdot 1000 \ \text{permil}$$

where the reference standard used here is PDB (Pee Dee Belemnite) $CaCO_3$.

Page 47, 5th line: $d^{13}C$ should read $\text{delta}^{13}C$.

The European Science and Environment Forum

Mission Statement

The European Science and Environment Forum is an independent, non-profit-making alliance of scientists whose aim is to ensure that scientific debates are properly aired, and that decisions which are taken, and action that is proposed, are founded on sound scientific principles.

The ESEF will be particularly concerned to address issues where it appears that the public and their representatives, and those in the media, are being given misleading or one-sided advice. In such instances the ESEF will seek to provide a platform for scientists whose views are not being heard, but who have a contribution to make.

Members are accepted from all walks of life and all branches of science. There is no membership fee. Members will be expected to offer their services in contributing to ESEF publications on issues where their expertise is germane.

Purpose of ESEF

The European Science and Environment Forum is a Charitable Company Limited by Guarantee (No.1060751). It was established in 1994 to inform the public about scientific debates. Our chosen method for achieving this objective is to provide a forum for scientific opinions that are usually not heard in public policy debates.

Our primary role is to provide an independent voice to the media, the general public and the educators, and by doing so, we aim to provide balance on scientific issues. A secondary role is to contribute to the scientific debate itself. Many of our authors will simplify papers that they originally wrote for the peer reviewed scientific literature. ESEF's tertiary role is to advise scientists how to present their findings to the media, and how the media will perceive, and may use, the information. We hope that this will provide dialogue and understanding between these two important institutions.

Formation of ESEF

ESEF was formed in 1994 by Roger Bate (Director of the Environment Unit at the Institute of Economic Affairs, London),

220

Dr John Emsley (Science Writer in Residence at Imperial College London University) and Professor Frits Böttcher (Director of the Global Institute for the Study of Natural Resources in The Hague). The issue of climate change was the initiation for the meeting. All three thought that the debate had been unduly one-sided and they wanted to provide a forum for scientists to publish their arguments for public consumption. The media, and via them the public, tended to only hear the so-called consensus view presented by government and intergovernmental science panels.

Of course climate change is not the only issue where member scientists consider that the media debate is not balanced and that there are many environmental and public health issues which are not fully discussed in the public arena either.

ESEF decided on a mission to provide the media and the public with accessible first-hand research of leading scientists in their fields, as an alternative to reports received from specialist journals, government departments or single-issue pressure groups. As Einstein is reputed to have said: 'Make science as simple as possible, but no simpler'. Our aim is to provide science simplified as far as possible. Our members are from fields as diverse as nuclear physics, biochemistry, glaciology, toxicology and philosophy of science. We intend on liaising between the media and our expert members to provide an independent voice on subjects germane to various public policy debates.

To maintain its independence and impartiality, ESEF accepts funding only from charities, and the income it receives is from the sale of its publications. Such publications will automatically be sent to members. Copies will be sent to selected opinion formers within the media and within government.

ESEF's address

4 Church Lane
Barton, Cambridge
England, CB3 7BE

Telephone: +44 (0)1223 264 643
Fax: +44 (0) 1223 264 645
Web: www.esef.org

Principles recommended for use in public policymaking

Much of the debate on science in the spheres of public health and environment centres around hazard assessment and the way that such assessment is used in public policy. We recommend adherence to the following principles for the use of science in public policy:

- Objectivity comes from open debate based on critical examination of evidence.
- Scientists will not always be able to provide unequivocal advice to policymakers; the boundaries of knowledge must therefore be clearly stated. and accepted as such
- Scientists, regardless of affiliation, should be able to provide policymakers with information to help in the definition of public policy priorities
- Scientific evidence should be judged on the consistency of the methodology and the accuracy of the data used, independently from the funding and explicit motivation of the scientist.

ESEF Committee

Prof. Dr Frits Böttcher The Netherlands
Dr John Emsley UK
Mr Roger Bate UK

Scientific Members of ESEF November 1997

Prof. Bruce Ames USA
Prof Tom Addiscott UK
Dr Sallie Baliunas USA
Dr Robert C. Balling US
Prof. Dr A. G. M. Barratt UK
Dr Jack Barrett UK
Dr Sonja Boehmer-Christiansen UK
Prof. Norman D. Brown UK
Prof. Dr K. H. Büchel Germany
Dr John Butler UK
Dr Francisco Capella Gómez-Acebo Spain
Dr David Cope UK
Mr Piers Corbyn UK
Prof. Dr. A. W. C. A. Cornelissen The Netherlands
Dr Barrie Craven UK
Mr Peter Dietz Germany

Dr A. J. Dobbs UK
Dr David Everest UK
Dr Oeystein Faestoe UK
Dr Patricia Fara UK
Prof Dr Hartmut Frank Germany
Dr James Franklin Belgium
Dr Alastair Gebbie UK
Dr T. R. Gerholm Sweden
Prof. Dr Gerhard Gerlich Germany
Dr Manoucher Golipour UK
Dr Adrian Gordon Australia
Dr Vincent R. Gray New Zealand
Dr Gordon Gribble USA
Prof Dr Hans-Eberhard Heyke Germany
Dr Vidar Hisdal Norway
Dr Jean-Louis L'Hirondel France
Dr Sherwood Idso USA
Dr Antoaneta Iotova Bulgaria
Prof. Dr Zbigniew Jaworowski Poland
Dr Tim Jones UK
Prof. Dr Wibjörn Karlén Sweden
Dr Terence Kealey UK
Prof. Kirill Ya. Kondratyev Russia
Prof. Dr. F. Korte Germany
Dr Johan Kuylenstierna Sweden
Dr Theodor Landscheidt Germany
Dr Alan Mann UK
Dr John McMullan UK
Prof. Dr Helmut Metzner Germany
Dr Patrick Michaels USA
Sir William Mitchell UK
Dr Paolo Mocarelli Italy
Dr Asmunn Moene Norway
Dr Brooke T. Mossman USA
Prof Dr Hans-Emil Müller Germany
Prof Dr Dr Paul Müller Germany
Dr Joan Munby UK
Dr Genrik A. Nikolsky Russia
Dr Robert Nilsson Sweden
Dr Eric Posmentier USA
Prof. Dr Harry Priem The Netherlands
Dr John Rae UK
Dr Christoffer Rappe Sweden

223

Dr Ray Richards UK
Dr Michel Saloman France
Dr Tom V. Segalstad Norway
Dr S. Fred Singer USA
Dr Willie Soon USA
Dr G. N. Stewart UK
Dr Gordon Stewart UK
Dr Lois Swirsky Gold USA
Dr Maria Tasheva Bulgaria
Dr Wolfgang Thüne Germany
Dr Alan Tillotson UK
Prof. Dr Karl Überla Germany
Prof. Dr H. P. van Heel The Netherlands
Dr Robin Vaughan UK
Prof. Dr Nico Vlaar The Netherlands
Dr Horst Wachsmuth Switzerland
Dr Michael P. R. Waligórski Poland
Dr Gunnar Walinder Sweden
Dr Gerd-Rainer Weber Germany
Prof Donald Weetman UK
Dr Charlotte Wiin-Christensen Denmark
Dr Aksel Wiin-Nielsen Denmark
Dr James Wilson USA

Business Members

Dr Alfred Bader UK
Mr John Boler UK
Mr Charles Bottoms UK
Dr Frank Fitzgerald UK
Dr Claes Hall UK
Mr Richard Hallett UK
Mr Peter Henry UK
Mr Holger Heuseler Germany
Mr Graham Horne UK
Dr Warwick Hughes Australia
Dr Kelvin Kemm South Africa
Mr Richard D. North UK
Mr Peter Plumley UK
Dr Brian Tucker Australia
Dr R. Wynne-Davies UK

Administrator

Lorraine Mooney

224

Author's addresses

S. L. Baliunas
Harvard-Smithsonian Center for Astrophysics
60 Garden Street
Cambridge MA 02138.
USA

Tel.:+ 1 617 495 7415
Fax.:+ 1 617 495 7049
email: sbaliunas@cfa.harvard.edu

Robert C. Balling, Jr.
Office of Climatology and Department of Geography
Arizona State University
Tempe, Arizona 85287
USA

Tel.:+ 1 602 965 6265
Fax.:+ 1 602 965 1473
email: robert.balling@asu.edu

Roger N. Bate
Wolfson College
Cambridge University
CB3 9BB
UK

Tel: +44 1223 263 529
Fax: +44 1223 264 643
email: 101627.2464@compuserve.com

Adrian H. Gordon
School of Earth Sciences
Flinders University
GPO Box 2100
Adelaide
5001
Australia

Tel: + 61 8 2012212
Fax: + 61 8 2012676
email: moahg@es.flinders.edu.au

Theodor Landscheidt
Schroeter Institute for Research in Cycles of Solar Activity
11227 Cabot Trail
Belle Côte, Nova Scotia B0E 1C0
Canada

Tel.: + 1 902 235 2281

David Wyndham Murray
Statistical Assessment Service
2100 L Street NW
Suite 3000
Washington DC
USA

Tel: + 202 223 3193
Fax: + 202 872 4014
email: STATS2100@aol.com

E. S. Posmentier
Departments of Physics and Mathematics
Brooklyn Campus of Long Island University
Brooklyn NY 11201
USA

Tel.: + 1 718 780-4163
Fax.: + 1 718 488-1465
email: eposment@titan.liunet.edu

Tom V. Segalstad
Mineralogical-Geological Museum
University of Oslo
Sars' Gate 1, N-0562 Oslo
Norway

Tel.: + 47 22 851 662
Fax.: + 47 22 851 656
email: t.v.segalstad@toyen.uio.no

S. Fred Singer
The Science & Environmental Policy Project
4084 University Drive, Suite 101
Fairfax, VA 22030
USA

Tel: + 1 703-934-6940
Fax: + 1 703-352-7535
email: ssinger1@gmu.edu

W. H. Soon
Harvard-Smithsonian Center for Astrophysics
60 Garden Street
Cambridge MA 02138
USA

Tel.: + 1 617 495 7415
Fax.: + 1 617 495 7095
email: wsoon@cfa.harvard.edu

Roy W. Spencer
Senior Scientist for Climate Studies
NASA/MSFC/GHCC
977 Explorer Boulevard
Huntsville, Alabama 35806

Tel: + 1 205 922 5960
Fax: + 1 205 922 5788

Robin Vaughan
Department of Applied Physics and Electronic & Mechanical
Engineering
University of Dundee
Dundee DD1 4HN
UK

Tel.: + 44 1382 344557
Fax.: + 44 1382 345415
email: r.a.vaughan@dundee.ac.uk

Gerd-Rainer Weber
Renatastr. 11
45130 Essen
Germany

Tel.: + 49 201 1805 380
Fax.: + 49 201 1805 437
email: gvst_URE.weber@t-online.de

Charlotte Wiin-Christensen
128 Chr.X Allé
2800 Kgs. Lyngbye
Denmark

Tel.: + 45 42 892255
email: fkomet@post7.tele.dk

Professor Dr. Aksel Wiin-Nielsen
Solbakken 6
3230 Graested
Denmark

Tel.: + 45 35 32 05 52
Fax.: + 45 35 36 53 57
email:awn@gfy.ku.dk

Index

Also published by ESEF in March 1996: *The Global Warming Debate*

For inquiries contact Lorraine Mooney, ESEF, 4 Church Lane, Barton, Cambridge, England, CB3 7BE
Telephone: (+44)(0)1223 264 643 Fax: (+44)(0)1223 264 645
E-mail: lorraine@esef.org   Web: http//:www.esef.org

What was said about *The Global Warming Debate:*
"The Global Warming Debate is a devastating exercise in imperial strip-tease. The many scientists who contributed to it are not prepared to go on telling the emperor he is fully clothed." *The Sunday Telegraph*.

"I do encourage you to read this book. You may not agree with the conclusions but I defy anyone not to have a nagging doubt about the arguments after doing so. No-one should be afraid of healthy debate in science." *International Journal of Climatology*.

"The ESEF report on global warming is essential reading for anyone who, like me, has been concerned that the science behind global warming theory lacks a firm foundation, and that the debate on this key issue has been so one-sided." *Professor Sir Geoffrey Wilkinson, Nobel Laureate for Chemistry 1973, Imperial College, London.*